Praise for *God, Shelby, and Me*

There are a multitude of precious gifts awaiting you, deeply woven into the words of this extraordinary and heart-warming journey. Animals are masterful teachers and author Joe Dwyer sits in the front row as their most beloved student. After reading this magical tale, you are left with absolutely no doubt as to the spiritual nature of animals. Joe, with the help of his beloveds, has delivered another treasure to our library."

—Rev. Drs. Craig & Kris Lecakes Haley, Department of Humane Religious Studies, Co-Chairs, Passmore Animal Chaplain Program, Instructors, Emerson Theological Institute

There are those among us born with acute sensitivity and compassionate empathy. Those destined to answer a divine call to action that requires deep courage and commitment to find and fulfill their purpose on earth. This book is destined to take you on a thought provoking spiritually enlightening journey with God, man and dogs. A must read for those who have compassion for animals and human frailty.

—Mary Cody, President Auntmarysdoghouse.com (a New Jersey based K9 Rescue)

It takes a sensitive, compassionate person who has developed empathy through their own suffering to be able to write about a relationship between God and a dog to help others; such a person is Joe Dwyer. This book highlights how God ministers to His animals and then uses them to minister to others. God knows all of our thoughts, speech and actions and sometimes He uses animals to get His message to us.

—Jan Fredericks, LPC, MA

Founder, God's Creatures Ministry,

Licensed Professional Counselor, Christian Author

God, Shelby, and Me told in the voice of canine sweetheart, Shelby, beautifully demonstrates that dogs have a special connection with the Divine. With open hearts, they fully embrace answering the call to help humans just when they need it most. Shelby, with special appearance by her canine brother, Daniel, eloquently portray their selfless gifts of guiding humans to their full potential — in this case, Joe — and then even more humans benefit through the determination of Joe, and brilliantly succeed in making the planet a better place for all. The gifts of Shelby, Daniel, and Joe leave a permanent imprint on the hearts of many and vibrates an uplifting energy out into the world—one we each need to continue to foster in order to bring more light and love to the world, so that all God's creatures can live in harmony together.

—Barbara Techel, author, intuitive oracle reader,

and soul nurturer for people and pets

"Powerful ...sensitive....honest ....and insightful testimony to God's interaction to and through His creatures."

—Monsignor Paul L. Bochicchio, St. Francis, Hoboken, New Jersey

I thoroughly enjoyed reading Joe's book. It was both edifying to Christ Jesus and brings awareness to the plight of abused and abandoned animals. As a lifetime rescuer, rehabbed and trainer, I am delighted to have been involved in rescuing Daniel the Beagle from the shelter in Alabama after he survived the gas chamber and his flight to NJ where he was ultimately adopted by Joe. It was a pleasure visiting Daniel in his home years later and meeting both Joe, his wife and Shelby. God bless all of them.

—Karen Rudolph, Schnauzer Savers Rescue

This is one of the best love stories I've ever read. Being an animal lover and dog mom of many, I often wonder how I got so lucky to find the dogs that have entered my home; how it was possible that we found each other. Joe shows us that everything, even our four legged friends, happen to us because of a higher power. This story of friendship, devotion, and the intimate connection we have to all living things, shows us that these are gifts from God. The healing power of animals is a true blessing and if you have never experienced that, or even if you have, this story will allow you to deeply feel the true beauty of the human-animal bond.

—Donna Rasulo, Dog Trainer, and President,

Rescue Haven Foundation

In the wake of one of the worst years and a half in many of our lives, Joe Dwyer's book, God, Shelby, and Me, reminds us that not all guardian angels have wings, but often times have fur. A great many times during this beautiful book, I was reminded of Clarence, the guardian angel from *It's A Wonderful Life*, who watches George Bailey's development and then comes to him in his time of need. Shelby is Joe's Clarence. Shelby enters Joe's life at the exact moment that she is needed, and this entrance reminds us about the beauty of God's plan. Though some of us (myself included at the moment) may have a hard time keeping the faith through certain situations, Shelby's entrance into Joe's world and the circumstances that surround it, remind us that God puts those we need in our path exactly when we need them. Thanks to Shelby, Joe, and this book, I will keep that message with me.

—Jamie Conway, High School English Teacher, Dog Lover

God, Shelby and Me takes you on a beautiful, personal, spiritual and heartwarming journey. Anyone who appreciates and loves their 4-legged companion will appreciate and love this story. Although some pages might move you to tears (as they did me), you will certainly be delighted that you purchased this book.

—Bruce Simon

As a devoted lover of all animals, big and small, I actively support Greyhound Dog Rescue of El Cajon, CA; Greyhound Rescue and Rehab of Westchester County, NY; Happy Tales Animal Sanctuary of NC, rescuing wild animals as well as abused farm animals; The Elephant Sanctuary of TN, rescuing elephants from circuses and zoos; The Sheldrick Wildlife Trust of Kenya, rescuing orphaned elephants and Hippos; as well as having served on the Board of Directors of the FernDog Rescue Organization

God, Shelby, and Me is a truly heartwarming and inspirational story that shows just how much we have to learn from dogs. It's a feel-good story that restores your faith and helps you believe that all people and all animals have a positive purpose on this earth. It draws you in from beginning to end and leaves you with positive thoughts and vibes for your own life.

—Kristen Miller, Teacher and Rescue Dog Momma

Joe's words, story, and Shelby's story, had me smiling and crying. I read the last 100 pages in one evening because I couldn't stop reading. I like the format, the conversations with God and the tie in with the Bible quotes and then bringing it all together with the affirmation. The story taught and comforted me at the same time. I had the experience of losing three faithful friends, two of which I held as they passed.

—Chris Osiega, Elementary School Technology Coordinator

This narrative takes you on a journey of the most loyal and purest of loves. A perfect depiction of the true connection we have with our pets and how animals truly are a gift to us from God.

—Christina Alamo, Middle School English teacher, animal lover

God SHELBY and Me

Book design by:

Arbor Services, Inc.

www.arborservices.co/

Printed in the United States of America

God, Shelby, and Me

Joe Dwyer

1. Title 2. Author 3. Pets/ Inspiration & Spirituality

Library of Congress Control Number: 2021918174

ISBN 13: 978-1-7378739-0-7

JOE DWYER

This book is dedicated to
the Divine Creator for His magnificent work in breathing life into the
animal kingdom. And to all who defend and protect one of God's most
precious gifts to humanity.

Contents

ACKNOWLEDGMENTS

To my parents, thank you for giving me life and a sustaining foundation of faith and love of God.

To my wife, Geralynn, thank you for your endless love, solidarity, and encouragement.

To my children, Joseph and Jenna, thank you for being the people you have become, for proving parenthood is a rewarding vocation, and for your love and friendship.

To my friend and editor, Nancy Genovese, thank you for your dedication to this book and my projects to help animals, and thank you for your love and respect for all God's four-pawed creatures.

To my Baby Girl Shelby, there are no words to thank you for all you have done for me and continue to do and for the priceless wisdom imparted. You truly are my soul dog.

To my Daniel, thank you for igniting my purpose to help animals in need and for teaching me the true significance and merit of a hero. Mostly, thank you for being my best "buddy."

Thank you to Spartacus, Greta, and Rommel, my delightful doxie trio for bringing love and laughter into my home while teaching many worthy life lessons.

To all who love, respect, value, and are grateful for animals—thank you for making this world a better place.

INTRODUCTION

The greatness of a nation and its moral progress can be judged by the
way its animals are treated.
~ Mahatma Gandhi

Since the age of two, dogs have secured a prominent place both in my mind and in my heart. Strange as it may seem, whereas most people have vague if any recollections of toddlerhood, my earliest memories date back to my second year of life. A capricious, strong-minded child, already fascinated beyond my years with dogs, I would sneak out of the yard in the spring and summer, eager to see my pal Bo, a playful black dog who loved my attentions, as I did his. I would giggle at his antics, screaming in delight when he crossed my path tickling my calf with his wagging tail; I dreamed of him and some of the other neighborhood dogs while asleep, and my waking reveries forever starred Bo and a host of other four-pawed creatures in the protagonist role.

Too young to realize at the time, I soon learned the Lord had entrusted me with the care, protection, and defense of His vulnerable creatures—dogs. In return I discovered in prayer that they would care for and protect me, not only through the upheavals, uncertainties, and tribulations of childhood and adolescence but long thereafter.

Thank God for dogs. Not only do I open my door to the four-pawed congregation offering a forever home, but as an animal rights advocate, I fight for them. Taking it further, I write about the precious dogs I loved

3

and love, to bring awareness to the canine condition and to the absolute blessings associated with feet and paws walking side by side.

God, Shelby, and Me is my latest book, and while it incorporates some of the roller-coaster rides of my life, the main theme features the amazing purpose of dogs living in harmony with human beings throughout life—mine in particular.

Needless to say, from early on I encountered conflicts with those who refute the idea of animals having souls. The Bible teaches that Jesus loves children and animals in a special way. Not long ago, the Holy Father, Pope Francis, during his Wednesday Audience in Vatican City, assured a little boy who had just lost his beloved dog: "Paradise is open to all of God's creatures." The Torah instructs with a code of laws authorizing animals to be treated with compassion.

Innocence and the state of being defenseless against harm warm God's heart in an exceptional way, a feeling I both understand and share. Consequently, to return to my discussion of the animal soul, logically speaking, there cannot be heaven without animals. Why? Simply because how can there be eternal bliss without our loving, faithful companions beside us?

It saddens me to note how some humans abuse and mistreat animals without even a guilty conscience. Just as mistreatment, violence, and neglect—be the victim a man, woman, or child—moves the Lord to tears, so does a dog that is beaten, starved, abandoned, and euthanized sometimes only months old because no one welcomes the puppy. I have given and will continue to give my life for the preservation of life and dignity in the animal world.

You will notice that my recently departed Shelby is the narrator of my book. An unusual, unique dog with the understanding, compassion, and empathy of a saint, she often seemed to be Mother Teresa (who I might add I had the pleasure of meeting) in a dog suit—not only to me, but to the many people of all ages she encountered on her brief life journey. My Baby Girl, as I called her, nurtured the troubled and the needy like a mother cherishes and fosters her children.

Granted, the end of her life was the will of God; nonetheless, her walk across the Rainbow Bridge to heaven was devastating for me, my family, and all blessed to know her. Not long ago a friend of mine told me, "Joe, when I received the news of Shelby's death, I cried like I never thought I would cry over a dog that was not part of my immediate family. Joe, I wept uncontrollably! Shelby was one of a kind!" Through my own tears, I had breath for just three words: "Indeed, she was."

Although within these pages, parts of my life will be highlighted, the true leading lady is Shelby. As you read, I urge you to bond with animals, discover the wonderful world of human-animal relationships, and bond with God, the creator of all life. Focus on the beauty of yesterday, the splendor of today, and a tomorrow in which we strive for the betterment of all living creatures. Look past all the adversity of the times, the political/social disagreements, and the devastating COVID-19 pandemic, and give neither power nor importance to these hard times. Remember, the divine intention is a loving family, friends, and animals living in harmony: This is the secret to a fulfilling, gratifying life for which to give thanks every day.

Besides love and sympathy, animals exhibit other qualities connected with the social instincts which in us would be called moral.

~ Charles Darwin

Peace and blessings

Joe Dwyer

CHAPTER I

Animals are God's creatures. He surrounds them with his providential
care. By their mere existence, they bless Him and give Him glory.
Thus, men owe them kindness.
~ Catholic Catechism 2416

My name is Shelby and I'm a pit bull, a breed sadly often misjudged and mistreated with the devastating bias of ignorance. Creatures of God, we can be neither ill-intentioned nor filled with malice toward others. Instead, we can be forgiving.

Though somewhat mysterious, we who live in faith believe in the afterlife. However, I was chosen to live several decades in the prelude to life. I know it sounds confusing, but in reality, it is rather simple. God allowed me to live spiritually, of course alongside the man who would be my savior, the man who God Himself hand-picked to fulfill a special mission to help animals and people in need, the man whom I would eventually save from a potentially catastrophic destiny.

It sounds complicated, even though I assure you it isn't. One thing is certain—the path of life is a two-way street. We give and we receive, we love and we are loved, and we are happy and we are sad. Best of all, if we are blessed as I am, we get to experience a journey walking side by side, crossing many different thresholds together.

I was told I was not yet born, and in the same divine breath I was assured I would be aware of certain happenings and people living on earth. When I questioned how this could be possible, God answered, making certain I understood that as one of His creatures I had a soul and a purpose. Did I comprehend my Creator's words? Not really. But with faith and patience, I would be enlightened.

Accepting God's will, I learn my first task is to keep my eyes on a little boy, a troubled, lonely child who often suffers bouts of melancholy. Obedient, I watch as the timid grade-schooler scratches his skin frantically, sometimes drawing blood. God only knows how desperately I want to lick his face to give him both emotional and physical relief. He seems frustrated and upset when his classmates ridicule his red welts. One day during noon recess in the playground, I watch as the children form a circle around him, scoffing at his skin condition, humiliating him at such a vulnerable age.

Much as youngsters sometimes do not realize the full implications of their deeds, the unkindness in early youth leaves indelible scars. I cry but feel powerless to intervene. His little face is tear-stained, and I know I could make him feel better. I ask God why humans hurt others, why they behave so foolishly at times. God's response is to wait—it is not yet time for me to gain certain knowledge. I think I have to live it before I can try to make a difference, which makes sense. If I can't relate to pain and misery, how can I be of help, feel compassion, and offer comfort?

The little boy fights off the aching mocking of others, running after school to see his pal, the black dog. To Bo, the boy's skin condition is nonexistent. The dog licks and kisses the red welts, seeing only the sweetness, hurt, and love nestled in his little friend's heart. This scene delights me, as I am a dog and I know the power we have in our hearts to love unconditionally. As I watch, it seems as if Bo is the only one capable of putting a smile on the school boy's face. Perhaps my now fourth grader will one day like me also. Little do I know that wishes do come true but not in accordance with our will. In the meantime I pray, asking God if I can help the little boy smile as Bo does.

"My child, it is not yet your time," God replies. "This little boy is not ready for his purpose with you. He must shed more tears, feel more sadness, and experience some of life's disheartening and seemingly irresolvable challenges before he will acquire the wisdom to step into the destiny I have designed for him. And you, my loving child, you also will have a cross to bear before you can help others carry their own. Be patient; the hour will be here when my plan unravels, and I will bring you both together for a beautiful mission. I know when the time is right. And I know you will trust me and abide by my wishes."

Everyone calls the little boy Joe. His name must be Joseph, like the earthly father of Jesus. He has to be special, but why is he so mistreated? My heart breaks when he stands alone crying. No one wants to play with him. What is the big deal? So what if he has red splotches on his face and arms. I don't care. I just want to run over to him, jump up on him, and kiss him. God, I will play with Joe. I know I have to wait, but it saddens me.

In his studies, Joe lacks self-confidence and self-esteem, a common effect of bullying. How can he feel good about himself with all the mockery? I wish children would not be so cruel. What they think is fun and laughter is anguish, sometimes with psychologically destructive consequences. God, I want to be there for Joe.

"My beautiful, sweet girl, I created you for Joe. But you must get to know him better, just like you must get to know me better. All my creatures should know God. Without this knowledge, there can be no love. Just be attentive to Joe. Watch how he handles his struggles. This, my sweet girl, is the first part of your mission."

Joe prays every evening. I cannot hear his words, but his eyes are lowered and he sits quietly. I hope God is listening. It's all about faith—that's easy. And it's all about understanding the Creator's waiting game—therein lies the challenge.

Then one autumn day several years later I see My Boy get into the car with his parents. He looks happy, which means they aren't taking him to school. Shortly thereafter they return. As they step out of the car, I notice Joe has a little dog in his arms. His face is glowing, and his steps have a new swing I have never noticed before. I am thrilled. During the following weeks, Joe seems to shed some layers. He's a different boy. His frown lines merge into a smooth brow, his lips tilt upward, and his shoulders straighten. His pace quickens and he learns the lesson of responsibility. Joe now has someone to care for. The influence of one tiny dachshund: the power of God's dog.

"Fritz . . . Fritz," I hear Joe call, giggling. Respectful, Fritz comes running, his tail wagging in the joyful spontaneity of childhood. I see the formation of a strong camaraderie between the two *boys*. The love they share warms my heart. It boomerangs between them. It's compelling. It's reassuring. Joe is no longer lonely in his thoughts and in his heart; he neither cries alone, nor do his ideas and thoughts fall unheard in the silence of solitude. A companion, a psychologist, and a mentor, Fritz fills the dreary void in Joe's life.

Prayers now have a voice. "Thank you, God, for Fritz—my brother and my best friend." I'm pleased Joe delves into gratitude. Blessings must be recognized as precious gifts.

Conversations follow—Joe's studies, his plans for the future, and of course girls. "Fritz, I'm not very popular. Maybe my skin condition makes me an undesirable date," he confides. I pray this little dog will help my special boy. It will save me the time needed to tackle more serious dilemmas once God gives me a breath. "Did you hear what I said, God? I'm waiting!"

"My dear Shelby, the moment will arrive. You are not yet ready for Joe, and Joe is not yet ready for you. There will come a time when he will need you. Now you must learn who Joe is; without this understanding, you will not be in a position to help him. You must learn patience. Life is a process. This is valid for all my children. I know best. Just trust me and be ready and available to respond when I summon you, regardless of where you may be."

Affirmation: Animals have souls. Listen when they speak: they impart much wisdom and love.

CHAPTER II

And the Lord restored the fortunes of Job, when he had prayed for his friends. And the Lord gave Job twice as much as he had before.
~ Job 42:10, ESV

With little Fritz in Joe's life, I notice he learns many valuable lessons that help him gain some of the God-given attributes he forfeited in his early youth, forfeited because of immaturity and inexperience. His school grades improve, he dates girls who truly enjoy his company, and he goes on to reserve a place in one of the colleges that has invited him to pursue a path to higher education. I had no idea dogs had the power to teach and heal, until I met Fritz.

I observe many changes in Joe. One, in particular, is the onset of apprehension mixed with anger and frustration. Something is disturbing his serenity. *God*, I ask, *what is wrong with My Boy? He has been sad in the past, but this new troublesome feeling seems overbearing at times. I want so much to help him.*

"My child, your purpose at the moment is to observe Joe and learn who he is. Trust me, this will be a help later on. Just be patient and very attentive to all Joe's feelings, actions, and thoughts. When the time is right, you will understand."

Although God's words seem to skirt my question, I obey His wishes. My focus is on Joe every waking hour. My eyes rarely close, not even when he sleeps. I listen to his conversations, to every word he pronounces. In my heart, I know I can help him smile.

One evening I hear Joe ask God why animals are abused. "God," Joe prays, "how can I help resolve this problem? Please show me the way. It is not fair. It is cruel and hurtful. I cannot stand by and watch the torture of innocent creatures. I know you share my sadness."

My heart is hurting as I listen to My Boy. Suddenly I understand why at times the light in his eyes dims and his brow furrows so intensely. Yes, it is unlike the sadness of his earlier years based on the bullying and personal attacks. This melancholy transcends all selfish feelings. It is no longer about poor Joe and his skin condition, or his fate as a victim, jostled with mean words in the school playground.

No, this is a changed sadness; his worrisome thoughts are focused on abused, neglected, and abandoned animals. His tears have a diverse flavor—tears shed for others, tears shed with compassion for God's creatures. Joe has learned brutality and the rage of evil often inflicted upon the vulnerable. In the gloom of my inability to help Joe, God smiles at me.

"My child," He begins, "you will soon have the answers. The blessings I grant you will sometimes confuse and other times frustrate and pain you, but in receiving my gift you will never stand alone. Did you listen to Joe's prayers? Didn't they seem different from his prayers of the past?

"My child, you heard Joe beg my mercy for maltreated animals. Did you notice that he did not ask for any favors for himself? His concern was exclusively for my defenseless creatures. His was a self-sacrificing prayer, a generous declaration of love. This act of devotion filled my heart with joy, as it mirrored my love and compassion for all my creatures. You see, my child, focusing on others in their times of need elevates purpose and intent above personal satisfaction and directs it toward others. My child, James 5:16 says, 'Pray for one another, that you may be healed' [NABRE]."

I watch as my boy demonstrates an optimistic mindset and perseverance during his college years, never slipping into the tempting *this is too difficult* or *I can't do this* attitude, which serves only to eliminate any possibility of success. His efforts are rewarded. He excels and moves forward into the professional world. I am so proud of him, my tail wags nonstop.

How wonderful. Thank you, God. But even if one stormy season clears into a sunny springtime, nature is temperamental and ever-changing, as all of life. Along the horizon, there will be more storms for My Boy, although on this day I see the glow as he receives awards and accolades in business, though still a young man.

Despite it all, something is missing from Joe's life. Nothing seems to truly fulfill him. Restless, I am unable to feel at peace. I do, nonetheless, pause badgering God with my prayers and questions about My Boy. And in my silence, I hear repeated echoes: "It is not good for the man to be alone" (Genesis 2:18, NABRE). What does God mean? What is He saying? Repeatedly He tells me to be patient, and so I shall wait for Him to explain in His own time, as always.

"My child, pay attention. Joe will soon experience one of the most beautiful blessings in life—love."

I notice My Boy is now dating a beautiful girl who seems to be delighted by his gallant attention. In return, he seems quite enchanted with her. A different situation, it holds me captive. I have never seen Joe so uplifted, though at times he seems to struggle and pray about doubts. My Boy confides in Fritz one evening, sharing his thoughts and considerations about marriage. However, the life-changing step scares him. "Is this girl the right one?" he asks Fritz. "Will she be the best mother for my children?"

"Lord, please give me a sign," Joe implores. With God and a tiny help from Fritz, he is in excellent hands. My Boy is a man of faith.

Alone in his room, I watch as Joe engages his furry brother in conversation. By far the best friend and confidante, the little doxie never gives any misguided advice. "Fritz, it's time I invite Geralynn to meet my parents, and more importantly you. I have fallen in love with her and intend to win her hand in marriage."

My eyes moisten. Again, I envy the short-legged doxie. I want to stand where he stands nuzzling My Boy's feet but quickly repent. I do not want God upset with me.

Several hours thereafter, I hear Joe on the phone with Geralynn and listen as he tells her about the evening's meeting. Curious, I wonder if they will bond or if Fritz will disappoint by coiling and withdrawing. I pray he will make My Boy happy.

"My child, have faith. Joe's love for Geralynn is powerful and integrally reciprocated. All My creatures deserve to be loved, cherished, and respected. I am the personification of all love. Never would I cast such unmarred love to the wind. Have faith, my child. Your time is fast approaching, but many tears will be shed first."

I do not like the last part of God's message, though I have to be trusting. I watch. I feel sorry for the little doxie. A lot of pressure is resting on his shoulders. But I pray and kept my faith unhinged. It is what God has asked me to do.

Nervous, I follow Joe around all day. Once Geralynn arrives, the die is cast. There is no turning back. In life, there is no reverse gear. Stepping into the living room, My Boy's love has an uneasy air regarding her. Who can blame the poor girl—a jury of three, parents plus Fritz all expected to pronounce?

Fritz sniffs her feet. Diffidently he lifts his gaze, locking eyes with hers. Joe stands at attention. My Boy is not breathing! What if? Sometimes faith is challenging and Satan has a sinister way to seed doubts. I refuse to succumb. God has put me here today for a reason.

But why is Fritz's tail frozen? I want to be there to offer reassurance to comfort Joe if something goes awry. My heart races. Why isn't he wagging his tail? Geralynn looks despondent. Fritz can't break her heart. God will not allow it, I pray. Suddenly the draft from the little doxie's tail waving at Mach 5 speed wafts across my nose! His tiny paws tremble then pirouette in delight. Leaning over, Geralynn extends her hands, gathering him in her arms. I hope she hasn't spent too much time applying makeup, I think as Fritz covers every inch of her face with a barrage of wet kisses. She is delirious with joy. My Boy rests his head in his hands, giving thanks. My prayer is answered. All three of us are in tears. Fritz is in love with Geralynn! Trust in the Lord.

"My child, your worries served no purpose but to upset your heart. 'Trust in the Lord with all your heart and lean not on your understanding; in all ways submit to him, and he will make your paths straight'" [Proverbs 3:5–6, NIV].

Affirmation: There is immense value in acquiring the patience of an animal. This gift reveals and helps you fulfill your true purpose.

CHAPTER III

Immediately after the distress of those days "the sun will be darkened, the moon will not give its light; the star will fall from the sky, and the heavenly bodies will be shaken."
~ Matthew 24:29, NIV

With a wife and infant son, My Boy has a pressing schedule. He seems to be overextending his energy resources from time to time, which causes me to worry. I question if perhaps Joe will no longer need my assistance and whether he has any spare moments to ponder the fate of animals at the hands of an unconscionable mankind with little respect for God's word or His creatures. It appears as if surrounded by his family, he may have developed a different life purpose.

I pray God will not redirect my mission. I am certain My Boy will never shut an eye on animals. But what if unexpected circumstances sidetrack his thoughts? God has told me to be patient. Am I disappointing Him? Will my slip of faith jeopardize my time with Joe?

"My child, why dwell on reckless doubts that serve no noble end? Your time is drawing near. Listen, watch, and learn. You too shall understand life's diverse paths—some thorny, some intertwined, and others smooth. Maybe you will regret your earthly mission, though there is great merit in overcoming obstacles. When I ask you to have faith, my intention is not for you to be unwavering in your belief. This is too easy. I challenge as my Son was challenged here on earth.

"My expectation includes the full submission of your mind and spirit. In so doing you can humbly entrust your will to me. I never promise a life of ease: there will be struggles and failings, disappointments and showers of tears. Did not my Son suffer for Joe? In return, Joe will face serious conflicts, but he will always defeat them. Soon, my child, he will engage my call. Again, I say to you—be patient."

God is all-loving and merciful, but sometimes it is difficult to understand why an evaluation of faith is synonymous with struggles, and why we question and fight instead of blindly accepting the reasoning behind the often-inexplicable trials sent. What does God mean—"soon he will engage my call"?

The sky is cloudy. A slight drizzle moisturizes the dry fall air. Despite the less than inviting climate, I know in keeping with the morning protocol, Joe and Fritz will step outside within minutes for their morning walk. When the door opens, I am surprised to see Joe carrying his furry brother in his arms, wrapped in a blue and white blanket. The strained knit of his brow betrays his concern. God, I hope nothing serious has happened to Fritz. My Boy seems unusually anxious.

But God has other plans for Fritz. His purpose has been fulfilled, his mission completed. Once in the car, Joe places the little doxie on the seat beside him. With one hand on the steering wheel and the other reassuringly caressing Fritz, he drives to a midrise building fifteen minutes distant. There is no tail wag, no kisses. In the pit of my stomach, several butterflies twirl around, lost. As uncertainty mounts, I imagine My Boy is sharing my uneasiness. The feeling scares me. What could be wrong? Why is Fritz so complacent?

"My child, you are about to learn an important life lesson. What is born blossoms, wilts, and dies: likewise, those we love and cherish."

What is God trying to tell me? His words are not comforting. I have to wait. Joe reaches a red traffic light, halts the vehicle, and leans over, gently lifting Fritz's blanket. "It'll be OK," he whispers in an attempt to shift the truth into something he secretly knows is wishful thinking—a desperate search for a miracle. Leaving the car, he walks over to the passenger side and gathers Fritz in his arms before entering the building. A grim look crosses his face. A wave of fear, like a sudden unexpected gale, whips past. *Please, God, help Joe and Fritz.* I pray and I wait. It's what I do best.

Joe exits alone, his shoulders bent, his gaze lowered. My Boy is crying. Sliding behind the steering wheel, he rests his head in the palms of his hands and sobs. Fritz, beloved brother and best friend, crosses the Rainbow Bridge, leaving Joe inconsolable: the devastating penalty unconditional love evokes.

My heart is pained—I want to run to Joe; I want to snuggle up to him, be there for him, but I have to be obedient to the will of God. This dutiful waiting does not silence my questioning. *Why, God? Why did you take Fritz from Joe?* The answer comes as always, assuming we are willing to pause long enough to listen. But we must interpret His words and learn from them since no one has knowledge of the unknown.

"My child, it is evident in Joe's anguish that I created you and all animals as creatures of pure love. Asking nothing but food, water, and the freedom to breathe some fresh air, my animals offer much in return. Not pleasure seekers but pleasure givers, their purpose is to love, comfort, console, and in some instances be of assistance in moments of need. Among the various animals, none has a selfish bone or self-serving thought. Once their basic needs are satisfied, their thoughts are all about others.

"Joe is heartbroken, his loss inconsolable. But my child, do not worry. Just continue to watch over him; I will take care of him in my way. Joe will never be without that special love."

Returning home, Joe explains about Fritz. "His illness was terminal; he was suffering and had come to the end of his life. God took him to heaven," he announces in a broken, choking voice to Geralynn. "I will never lose sight of his delightful, loving personality. I was truly blessed to have him in my life and to have you in his life even if for just a brief moment time. As Job 1:21 says, 'The Lord gave and the Lord has taken away.'" Many tears are shed for Fritz, in addition to my own.

Affirmation: Lasting gratitude is found by cherishing every day and every gift, especially those wrapped in fur.

CHAPTER IV

Two are better than one, because they have a good return for their labor: If either of them falls down, one can help the other up. But pity anyone who falls and has no one to help them up.
~ Ecclesiastes 4:9–10, NIV

Although My Boy, together with Geralynn, fathers two beautiful children while cultivating a successful business career, he seems not quite satisfied at times; something is not yet in place to give rise to the life flow harmony he aspires to. Perhaps his purpose is not clearly defined. To me it is evident: something is adrift in My Boy's mind and not yet within his reach. He seems to be grasping for an answer. I notice he prays quite often during quiet moments, which are somewhat of a luxury in his day.

Nonetheless, he learns to address God while driving, showering, or whenever he finds himself alone once the lights are dimmed and the echoes nonexistent. During these special conversations, his demeanor is tense, leading me to believe the discussions are serious. Puzzled, I know all will be revealed to me in due time. But this request for patience is not easily accepted. However, I don't want to disappoint with noncompliance.

"My child, Joe has been enriched with the gospels and the teachings of Jesus. Empowered, he feels compelled to evangelize in his own way, free from confining restrictions. In so doing he will quench his thirst to help others grow in divine knowledge and lead happier, more rewarding lives. You see, my child, in a sense Joe is a savior, driven to save not only animals but anyone entrenched in a personal dilemma.

Sadly, however, he is incapable of pulling himself up when he stumbles. This, my child, is why I am sending you to him."

My heart is racing. I feel my tail wag almost out of control. God has not had a change of mind. I was wrong to doubt His word. I will be with My Boy. If only . . . if only I would not have to wait so long!

"My child, your sweet innocence has given me the gift of a hearty laugh. You will soon understand that life is not lived in an ever-blooming garden. You have not yet reached the crosswalks of life. But listen carefully to my words. No one can make the journey unassisted, though some may believe they can. I let them, as I give free will to all. However, when they stumble, fall, and ask for help, they will be carried. Just because Joe is a man of faith does not mean the voyage will be smooth sailing. Now he will need me to walk beside him more than ever."

I'll admit that some of God's messages leave me confused, although I do have the feeling I will soon meet My Boy. Unknown to me is the whirling vortex of quarrel and disagreement, a conflictual cavity into which Joe will soon be drawn.

"My child, it is time. The pathway may not be easy, the days may seem dark and empty, but never falter in your faith. Yours is a mission based on learning through experience. If you do not hurt, you will not understand when Joe hurts. If you don't face the tyranny of bias and injustice, you will not be a good witness to those ridiculed or treated unfairly.

"Your own encounters with life will ready you to give of yourself for the benefit of others. Hardships and obstacles are the alleyways to mercy and compassion through a strengthening of faith. But when you ask for my intervention, I will place a hand on your head. In return, you will channel your gratitude for my blessing by comforting first

Joe and then others in need. **During your walk on earth, my child, never lose your trust in me. Instead, learn to lean on me. There is no dishonor in frailty. Amid trials and turbulence, you will learn life, and I will be alongside you whenever you summon me."**

If I thought I was confused before, now I am befuddled and in the dark. I know with certainty I have faith. All the rest is shrouded in mystery—all but Joe. I just can't wait to walk beside him. Once the voice of God quiets, my heart races with the anticipation of meeting My Boy.

Cast your cares on the LORD and he will sustain you; he will never let the righteous be shaken.

~ Psalm 55:22, NIV

A quick interlude of quiet interrupts me. I awaken somewhat confused about my whereabouts. Where is the glowing, uplifting light? Where are the warmth and outstretched protective arms that have kept me secure and safe? Have I been abandoned? Did I commit a wrong to upset God? I know I am impatient to be with My Boy, but I don't think this is the reason for my banishment. Where are you, God? Will you speak to me again?

"My child, be calm. Your mind is causing you to doubt. This is what happens on earth. You will learn lessons by experiencing and overcoming obstacles. It will be learning by trial and error. I have neither abandoned you nor relinquished my hold on you. I do not desert my creatures, even if in dire moments it might seem as if I am not present. If you silence your thoughts, you will hear my comforting words. As promised, I will be with you always, walking side by side with you, especially when you feel forsaken. This is a test you have to pass. You begged to meet Joe, and now the time has come. Initially,

you will need him for survival; eventually, you will repay the favor when he falls in need. But you must first overcome this hurdle."

Although God's words are reassuring, the serenity seems different. He speaks about a hurdle and learning by trial and error. I'll admit I'm scared, but I believe in His mercy.

I am among other young pups and a large female dog who I believe is my mother. Though in uncertain surroundings, I quickly find my bearings, thus gaining familiarity as the pups nuzzle me. My mom gently licks my head. I feel the pleasant emotion of belonging. I am safe, comfortably nestled against my mom's warm belly.

Suddenly I'm lifted and handed to a man who grabs me roughly, squeezing my side. A strange feeling churns in the pit of my stomach. Thrown into the back seat of a car, I hear voices, harsh voices speaking words I have never heard before, angry words. What does it all mean—and where are they taking me? I decide to focus on God's purpose for me. Hopefully, I will soon meet My Boy and fulfill the Creator's plan for my life.

Once again, I am lifted and heavily dropped into a large wired pen with other dogs. Observing my surroundings, I realize I am not welcome. My pen mates are covered with soot and some red spots—dried blood, I think. One large dog approaches and bites me on the nose. His teeth are sharp and dig belligerently into my skin. Ouch! This pain is a new sensation—disturbing. Another dog jumps deliberately on my back, forcing me to fall on my side, injuring me with the impact of his weight. *God, please help me!* I cry inside. *What is happening? I have committed no wrong against these animals. Why are they causing me suffering?*

Father, forgive them for they know not what they do.
~ Luke 23:34, ESV

"My child, sometimes harsh and merciless deeds committed in the world are difficult to understand. Animals are kind and gentle souls, born to give unconditional love. Committed to loyalty, they befriend men, women, and children. It is their reason to be. Yet tragically they are often trained and used for malicious gain. They have no fault.

"Just continue to walk in faith. Always believe in salvation regardless of how much darkness is before you. Remember the words of St. Teresa of Avila: 'Let nothing disturb you; Let nothing frighten you, all things are passing away: God never changes. Patience obtains all things Whoever has God lacks nothing; God alone suffices.'"

I repeat the calming words of St. Teresa. Tears run down my face as I watch a group of surly, unkind men torment several dogs, one at a time. Brusque and punitive, the tone of their voices scares me. Observing for a while, I notice the calmer dogs upset the men. Anxious and frustrated, they growl and sneer while enticing the pups into aggression. Brutal beatings draw trickles of blood. My legs burn. Sweet, docile dogs turn into beasts of violence, all for the financial gain netted through devastating pit bull fights!

Do not fear: I am with you; do not be anxious: I am your God. I will strengthen you, I will help you, I will uphold you with my victorious right hand.
~ Isaiah 41:10, NABRE

Filled with a love of God, I pray for redemption against the snares of all that is not good. I fight hard not to incur a personality change at the hands of diabolic men. Certain I was not born to fight, I hold onto the hope rising in my heart, the hope God has planted.

Realizing I am too meek and mild to harm another, I'm labeled useless and cast aside. In my heart I know I was born for a special mission—to comfort, not to antagonize; to heal, not to harm; to love, not to hate. Perhaps they understand my way is peace, not combat; perhaps they don't.

Regardless, with a long, abrasive noose fastened around my neck, I am dragged to the car. After a short ride, I am hauled like wet batch and stone and tightly knotted to a fence. It's a cold wintry night. The wind howls. I'm given neither food nor water, just kicked and cruelly abandoned. People pass in cars, some in trucks, lots of people from time to time with children and even dogs. I soon discover that I have been discarded at a gas station!

Echoes of animated voices, occasionally laughter, encourage me to yelp for help. Not a head turns in my direction; not a gaze meets mine. Invisible, I seem to not even exist. Terrified, hungry, trembling, and lonely, I seek my one friend—God. The stabbing pain in my legs begins throbbing. The muddle in my head worries me. "My God, my God, why have you forsaken me?" (Psalm 22:1, NIV). Even the Son of God cried out. Why, God? Did I offend you in some way?

"My sweet child, you have not been forsaken. I gave you my word, and I never default. You are learning about the consequences of depression in suffering. To help Joe and others, you must live hardships. This experience will grow the love, compassion, and empathy I have seeded in your heart. Trust me and have faith in my words. It is now time!"

Much as dark clouds obscure the sky, I feel a sprinkle of icy rain; I see a star—the star behind which I stand in anticipation.

Affirmation: When God calls, answer; but remain vigilant, since He may call again.

CHAPTER V

The Lord is my strength and my shield, in whom my heart trusts. I am
helped, so my heart rejoices; with my song I praise him.
~ Psalm 28:7, NABRE

I am so cold. The pain in my hind legs persists, stabbing yet spasmodic, with
brief eye-blinking moments of reprieve. Without nourishment, my strength
is seeping away. I can hardly stand, though I don't have an alternative to
lie down. Drops of rain are pelting heavily, quickly drenching the ground,
turning the sand mixed with pebbles into cold, abrasive mud.

I thought I was going to meet Joe; what could have gone wrong? Maybe
I have displeased God, offended Him. I didn't have any bad intentions. Is
this how my time here will be spent?

I don't want to lose faith, but everything seems so bleak, and I am
not sure how long I will endure or if I even want to. Is this my purpose?
It seems so meaningless. What is the point of being fastened to a fence
assaulted by a deluge of icy rain, without food and water? Why don't any
of these people notice me? I am crying for help. And the awful pain—why
did those dogs attack me so brutally? I had no fault. I had just arrived from
heaven. As Job surrendered his life to God, so too will I.

Then Job answered the LORD and said; I know that you can do all
things, and that no purpose of yours can be hindered.
~ Job 42:1–2, NABRE

God, are you still with me?

29

"My beautiful child, I hear you in prayer, though sometimes it appears as if I am distant. I am sorry for your pain and anxiety. You asked to come here, therefore you must learn about the life you have chosen. As a gift at birth, I give everyone free will. If mankind decides to opt for the virtuous path and proceeds along an honorable journey, he has the ability to succeed; but if he prefers the unethical and the journey of a villainous, unconscionable person, he has the same ability to do so. When I see one of my creatures paying the consequences for another's poor decision, I give extra love. Never stray from your purpose, and be strong in your faith. A new beginning is upon you."

I believe and trust in God. I do, however, pray I will survive the night. My Creator expects me to go forward in the strength of my faith. I will not disappoint Him.

I feel a sudden warmth, though the stiffness in my legs makes standing painful. The night darkness is turning into a burst of light. A circular form lifts from nowhere and rises from behind the horizon into full view in the sky. I have seen it before. Joe would gaze at it in the early morning while walking Fritz. Perhaps God sits behind the sunrise.

My Creator is here this morning. I see Him, though the red fireball is almost uncomfortably bright. I shut my eyes. The sound of footsteps brings me to attention. A woman is approaching, a woman with a kind face.

"Hello," she greets, smiling. "I won't hurt you. Are you alone, or do you belong to someone?"

I was abandoned. I'm hungry, thirsty, and in pain. I am supposed to meet Joe. Maybe God will allow her to hear my words.

She walks closer, then abruptly halts. Why is she pulling away? Maybe she notices I am a pit bull. It's so unfair. Prejudice is wrong. Racial and breed profiling highlights ignorance and harms the hearts of those misjudged.

Why would anyone want to cause pain and distress? But I think this might be part of my purpose—to exonerate the pit bull from faulty labeling and to stop the sting of nasty, unkind words.

"I'd like to come closer," she says.

Why is she suddenly so tense? *You can come closer. I will not hurt you*, I reassure, praying my words will be convincing. I am new at this and somewhat fearful. But she moves closer and pats me on the head. No one has ever done that before, and it feels special.

"I will take you with me. You will be inside and have food and water."

She keeps her word and unfastens the rope. I pray my legs will be strong enough to get me to her car. All I want is to finally meet My Boy and give him all my unconditional love.

The car ride is smooth; just several stops for red lights until the kind lady announces, "Here we are." I don't know where I am, but many other dogs are walking around. I am served a bowl of food and some water. It feels good to have something in my stomach and not feel my tongue so dry. Every so often a human passes. I wish I could speak with them, show them how much I would love them. I don't get the chance. Maybe when I meet Joe my life will change.

"My child, I created you and all animals with the desire to give love even before receiving it. Trust me—the time is near. Although Joe knows of the love capacity in animals, through your empathy and compassion he will be able to show others and to share your forgiving heart with all. Together you and Joe will be my emissaries, filling the hearts of many children, teens, and adults suffering ills of body, mind, and spirit; ills of unkindness, prejudice, and bullying with the meaning and passion of my commandment: 'Love one another. As I have loved you, so you also should love one another' [John 13:34,

NABRE]. My child, your beautiful, pure soul will radiate through your eyes, kindling love in all who meet you."

I am trying to be polite and stand when someone approaches despite my agonizing pain. Everyone is pleasant, and I am learning that not all humans are hurtful. Meanwhile, unbeknown to me, God is planning a big surprise!

One afternoon, while I rest in the rear of my cage, feeling safe even if a bit lonely, a man approaches. "Hello, Shelby," he greets. His voice is soft, mellow, rather soothing. It is a tone I have never heard before, almost endearing. Timid, I do not raise my head. I have no idea I am named Shelby. Another man hurt me so badly when he slammed his fists against my legs. Can I trust?

"Hi, Shelby," he repeats. I lift my eyes to meet his.

O, God, I gasp, *it's Joe, it's My Boy! I would recognize him anywhere—I saw him grow up. Thank you, God. Please let him like me, even a little.*

"My child, I told you the time would come when you would see Joe. This is the right moment. Although he will save you, you will give him his life. Yes, my child, Joe needs you desperately, more than ever."

Tears well up in my eyes. My heart races. What if I cannot be who God wants me to be? What if I fail? Will My Boy be scared because I am a pit bull? Will he believe the fraudulent voices that define us as dangerous? God, I am a little scared!

"My child, take my yoke upon you, and learn from me; for I am gentle and lowly in heart, and you will find rest for your souls. For my yoke is easy, and my burden is light [Matthew 11:29–30, ESV]."

I will believe not only because God asks me to have faith, but because My Boy is here. I must have patience. *Please, God, give me patience . . . and before I end, please let him love me, even a tiny bit!*

"Little do you know, my child—if only you knew!"

Affirmation: The opinions and behaviors of others are not always valid and kind; however, they can open your eyes and pave the way to great things. Stay strong and true to yourself!

CHAPTER VI

For I know well the plans I have in mind for you—oracle of the Lord—
plans for your welfare and not for woe, so as to give you a
future of hope.
~ Jeremiah 29:11, NABRE

In the quiet of night, I hear the rustlings of several restless dogs trying to get comfortable for the evening's rest. Much as I feel safe here and am given nourishment, I cannot lose sight of the fact that I am in a shelter for abandoned animals. The attendants who care for us are sweet and affectionate, but the memories of mistreatment and neglect linger.

Though my faith is strong, it is difficult to understand why a handful of humans find it hard to have some love and respect for us as innocent creatures of God. Do they think we are punching bags for their anger, frustrations, or hostilities? Or is it just a power strategy to camouflage feelings of inferiority? Often, I question why my legs were injured and why I was discarded because I rejected violence for money in fighting other pit bulls!

I remain hopeful that in time I can overcome my early life trauma and perhaps move forward with My Boy to prevent others from living my hell. But God has told me He gave humans the gift of free will. All I want is to comfort all who suffer. *God, please let me fall asleep to stop my thoughts and past remembrances. I have a hunch My Boy will return tomorrow. Please, God, help me win his heart.*

"My child, all will happen as promised. You are almost there. Pay attention to your surroundings. My creatures deserve better. You and Joe will be my spokespeople, and soon you will have a new brother! Every pendulum swing of the clock is a trial of patience. Even taking a deep breath and counting to ten will stretch your nerves. Again, be patient, my child."

Rejoice in hope, be patient in tribulation, be constant in prayer.
Romans 12:12, ESV

The following morning, shortly after breakfast, My Boy arrives. With determined steps, he walks right in front of my cage. For a split second, my faith in myself wanes. In its place stands self-doubt, a reluctance, an uncontrollable hesitation to put my best paw forward. Joe approaches. His smile, so flirtatious, holds me frozen in the rear of the cage. My reticence is not about misgivings or distrust—not with My Boy. I trusted him years before I came to be on this planet.

I think it is fear, an overpowering emotion that cripples, a reaction to life and others, serving only to present myself mistakenly. Joe walks closer. I inch myself farther back in the cage, hurting my tail against the metal framework. By nature, I am not a jump-all-over-you dog, but a shy, more reserved pup. I trust My Boy will know how to read me and won't get the wrong impression: *Please, God . . .*

"My sweet child, sometimes my creatures squander energy on meaningless concerns. I made Joe in my image as a man with love in his heart—a love for humankind. And I will tell you a secret, my child. When I created Joe, I infused him with an abundance of love for my special creatures, animals. Accordingly, I designed his purpose around this gift. Therefore, there is no need for useless fretting. You

will see. Again—all in due time. Remember my words: 'Pray for him and be patient just a tiny bit longer.'"

When God speaks, I listen. In the company of My Boy since childhood, I know he loves animals, but getting God's confirmation is a miracle, considering my first earthly experiences with humans.

Maybe My Boy is on his way. I lick my paws clean just in case I will receive a blessing. My morning hygiene is barely completed; I feel someone observing. Dare I raise my eyes? Trust in the Lord.

"Hi, Shelby," My Boy greets. "How are you today?"

How am I? I'm in heaven again here in Joe's company. His eyes are on me, sweet eyes laced with a thin thread of melancholy. Immediately he wins my love. Now I pray God will help me with my fear. After a few minutes he relaxes; his face is no longer tense. *Why?* I question. I am about to find out.

"Shelby, let's go for a little walk." Though my legs hurt without reprieve, I do not want to refuse his invitation. What if he interprets my reluctance as a rejection? Slowly rising to my feet, I step out of the cage once the door is opened. I try my best to walk without whimpering or excessive limping. Several minutes later, Joe pauses in front of a bench. It is a warm, balmy day and the sun feels comforting on my back.

My Boy suspects I am in distress. Already we seem to have a special connection. "Let's sit a while, Shelby, and get acquainted. Would you like that?" I wag my tail leisurely. Though it's not an exhilarated, wide-sweeping wag, My Boy understands. As we sit, he tries to caress my face. I freeze but do not turn away. Joe would never hurt me as the other men did. Joe has love in his eyes.

I am learning about My Boy's family, though honestly, I already knew them even before I came to earth. As he speaks, I wonder if I will ever have the pleasure to meet them. Will his wife Geralynn come here for a visit? Attentively I listen to every word about his two children, Joe Jr. and Jenna, and his three rescue dogs, Rommel, Greta, and Spartacus. He is so charming. Every few minutes I turn to meet his glance. Chills run along my spine.

"Shelby, I have told you a bit about myself. Now may I ask what happened to your legs? I can see you are in great pain."

I smile when My Boy calls me Shelby. It's a pretty name, though I know I was named Shelby because I was found fastened on the outskirts of a Shell gas station.

Joe notices my agony much as I try to conceal my suffering. *I think I was snatched from my mother and siblings to be trained as a bait dog for larger pit bulls to attack. They take pups and turn them into moneymaking commodities for personal gain. I was beaten and then thrown to the aggressive dogs. Despite it all, I hold no rancor toward those other pit bulls. It was not their fault. They too were violently abused and forced into combat mode.*

I see My Boy's eyes well up as I speak. It's amazing how we can communicate. It saddens me that I am adding to his already heavy thoughts. Still, he makes time to visit me and inquire about my state of being. No one has ever cared before. Now I want to care for him. Something is troubling My Boy. *Please, God, let him confide in me. I want to help him.* He understands I was brutally mistreated—the source of my painful crippling injuries. And I understand his mission is to fight for animals to live dignified lives in loving homes.

"My child, you are in the right place at the right time. I am counting on you now to stay close to Joe. Pay attention to his words, but more so to his heart. You may not understand yet, but soon you will."

Initially, God's message puzzles me. It almost seems cryptic. Then early one morning My Boy comes to visit. Much as he tries to smile, his jaw remains taut. I gaze at him with questioning eyes, eyes that reassure him I am here to listen. *Forget my pain, Joe; yours is more torturous.*

Our bond is strengthening. I can feel the attachment forming. This morning our relationship takes on a new dimension. Joe reads my eyes and asks me to sit beside him on our favorite bench. "Shelby," he begins, clearing his throat, "I am despondent." My heart feels heavy. He tells me about his firm commitment to a code of morals and ethics and how in some professional arenas it is not always honored. "Shelby, this goes against who I am and what I stand for. I must be true to myself regardless of the price I will pay."

I learn that My Boy tries to uphold the Commandments and follow a path of love and healing. "And walk in love, as Christ loved us and gave himself up for us, a fragrant offering and sacrifice to God" (Ephesians 5:2, ESV).

"Unfortunately, humans stray, dear Shelby. And humans have a wide variety of perspectives on any given point—all humans. It is a trait of the human condition. As it is written: 'There is no one who understands, no one who seeks God . . . all have sinned and are deprived of the glory of God' [Romans 3:11, 23, NABRE]."

Although Joe assures me that he always follows his conscience, others misunderstand certain actions because their viewpoints differ. Ultimately, stubborn minds fold into miscomprehensions that spread to uncontrollable proportions. At that point, all sense of equity and fair play is lost, turning dedicated men of integrity into victims.

Visibly upset, my heart pains for him. From the corner of my eye, I detect a tear as it slips down his cheek. Ever so slowly, he turns his head, perhaps hopeful I won't notice. I do. Nothing escapes me about Joe. I know My Boy better than he can imagine, and one day I will be strong enough to lick away his tears and, God willing, be a comfort through his heartaches and disappointments. *Please God, hear my thoughts this morning.*

Affirmation: Relationships created by God are a cherished gift to both parties involved and to those who are blessed to witness and benefit from the special connection.

CHAPTER VII

Beware of false prophets, who come to you in sheep's clothing, but
underneath are ravenous wolves.

~ Matthew 7:15, NABRE

I know Joe is hurting, yet, powerless, I am unable to comfort him. *God,*
this is so frustrating. Why am I still not in a position to help My Boy? He
seems so distraught. What is happening, God? Why is he anxious and
troubled? Maybe if I know why, I can be of assistance?

"My dear child, life here among my creation is about forming and
maintaining bonds based on love, respect, and trust. The bond of love is
what pleases me most. Unfortunately, these bonds are not indestructible,
thus fragile and delicate, they can easily rupture. Sadly, this failing
is in various aspects of life. However, true and enduring faith arises
exclusively within and through me in the relationship I create. You
and Joe will connect in a special way, a connection that will exercise
an empowering impact not only on you both but on many others."

I always feel reassured after my conversations with God. After all, I
trust no one but Him, though I am starting to feel something different for
Joe. Several months have passed and My Boy is a faithful visitor, arriving
always with, at minimum, the ever-slightest trace of a smile. I discover that
when I wag my tail, his smile widens, illuminating his face. He knows how
to captivate me, especially when he arrives late, full of apologies for being
remiss. What he doesn't know is that his lateness is irrelevant.

Standing outside my cage, Joe is speaking to one of the women who care for all of us. "I want Shelby to have a nice home," he says, "where she will be treated with the love, respect, and dignity she deserves. It is my feeling that she has been treated inhumanely and viciously abused. Look at her legs: it's heartbreaking!"

When you come upon your enemy's ox or donkey going astray, you must see to it that it is returned. When you notice the donkey of one who hates you lying down under its burden, you should not desert him; you must help him with it.

Exodus 23:4–5, NABRE

"Joe, Shelby is a pit bull. Unfortunately, they are not a top priority on the adoption list. People fear their notoriety and believe they are vicious," the woman responds.

"But it is just a senseless myth," My Boy blurts anxiously, "a myth based on breed ignorance. I want to educate people to make fair decisions that have roots in truth. Any creature trained into combat mode will behave accordingly. However, by nature, all domestic animals are pacifists, born with the unconditional love gene."

"Joe, you are an inspiring spokesperson and defender of all four-legged creatures. Maybe your passion and willingness to debunk pure hearsay will change the tide."

"I will certainly do my best. Just look at Shelby. Judging from her injuries, she has been severely abused, yet she is submissive, almost timid. She has not allowed man's wickedness to wreak havoc with her personality and values."

I listen to the conversation between Joe and the nice lady, but I don't want to be adopted because then I will no longer see My Boy. This saddens me.

"**My child, don't waver in faith. Remember, you are here for a purpose. I created you for a specific reason. Nothing in life is without a scope. Again—be patient.**"

God is testing me again. How patient do I have to be? When will it all come to be as my Creator wishes?

The season is turning. Gone is the bitter cold that intensifies my pain. "Hi, Shelby," Joe greets. My heart beats at double speed. "I came to say hello. I am in a bit of a rush today, but let's sit awhile outside."

I know he is dressed differently. His demeanor is more somber. I feel Joe is hurting. *Thank you, God, for bringing him to me today. Maybe I can help.* We stroll under the still-barren trees. The early spring air feels soothing. Once in the sun, I notice the tears. My breath pauses. *God, I hope My Boy is not going to speak bad news. Please allow me to comfort him. My heart is breaking.*

"**My dear Shelby, Joe is a good, honorable man. Like all of my creatures, he does slip up at times, nothing serious, but in the core of his being, he is full of compassion and nurturing. Above all, my child, he loves you. Life is a learning process, and Joe also must cross a path laden with obstacles while trying to build harmony as he balances his professional life with his wife and two children, his commitment to advocate for animal dignity, and the right to life. If he keeps his perspective in focus, he will see the path ahead. But, my child, the road ahead will be extremely challenging. Herein rests your mission.**"

God is our refuge and strength, a very present help in trouble.
Therefore we will not fear though the earth gives way,
though the mountains be moved into the heart of the sea.
~ Psalm 46:1–2, ESV

My mission? I wonder what God has in mind. Then the openness—the outpouring, unburdening of My Boy's mind. Joe speaks to me about a brief leave of absence. His tears flow. He digs in his pocket, perhaps for a Kleenex, but his hand exits empty. I know I could lick his tears away but don't dare cross the line. It will remain my secret, shared only with God.

"Shelby, I will be going away for a couple of days. When I return, I will take you home." His face lights up in a smile, a contagious smile. Though I do not understand, my tail wags in joy. When My Boy is happy, I am absolved of all my pain and sadness. Quickly Joe leans over and kisses the top of my head. I tremble in raptures. No one has ever shown me such tenderness! *Thank you, God!*

Much as I am lonely in Joe's absence, I do not go for walks. My appetite wanes. However, the memory of Joe's first kiss is my life-sustaining nourishment. It has taught me to hope. I pray for Joe, for the blessing to see him again. Prayers are always answered if wrapped in faith—even if, all in God's time.

And God's time does arrive. This morning shortly after breakfast, Joe walks past my cage with a pleasant lady. "Shelby, I'm going to take you outside awhile." The door to my cage is open. I pray my legs will not betray me. By now I understand that my purpose is to lead others into peace, not to be a catalyst for anxiety. The pain is throbbing, perhaps because of my inactivity while My Boy was absent.

It seems as if there has been moisture in the air. Maybe it rained during the evening. In repentance, the sun is peeking from behind an odd-shaped elongated white cloud. I notice three little dogs who all resemble each other with their long bodies and short legs. Joe and I approach the pups. I pause. Hopefully they will not bite me as the other dogs whipped into aggression.

"Shelby, meet Rommel, Greta, and Spartacus—part of my family." Joe beams proudly. "You will love them as I do."

I recognize the beautiful lady with dark wavy hair. She's Geralynn, Joe's wife. I try not to whimper, to ruin this happy moment for My Boy. Quietly I sit beside his feet. It's not exactly brain fog, but I am somewhat unclear about these circumstances. Should I say something? Are they expecting me to sniff them? A man of acute intuition, Joe reassures me everything will be just fine. I desperately want to believe, but my gut feeling is gnawing. Mine will be a joy mixed with sadness, though certainty is not more than an inkling.

As the car comes to a halt, I pray. *God, please be with me. Don't let me do anything to upset anyone.* In times of need, He listens.

"Shelby, we are home!" Home? Do I hear My Boy correctly? Does this mean I am going to live with Joe and his family and his three dogs with long bodies and short legs?

"Come on in, Shelby," My Boy invites. "We'll have something to eat and all get acquainted. I know you will love your sister and brothers. They know all about you and are waiting to finally meet you. Rommel and Greta will adore you. Spartacus is the alpha male, but you will charm him in time."

I pray no one notices my rising apprehension. My Boy does. "Don't worry, my Baby Girl," he whispers, caressing my head. I am delirious. Joe has called me his Baby Girl!

In the dark of the middle of the night, I hear the choir: Rommel, Greta, and Spartacus breathing in deep sleep. I feel safe for the first time in my life. My bed is so soft that my legs hurt less. He is sweet, My Boy. I can't wait to know him better. *Keep him well*, I pray.

During the bleakness of the night, God whispers: **"My child, you are finally home, in a house where love rules. This is my wish for** all of creation—to love, be loved, and grow in faith while living a compassionate, noble family life. I destined you a member of Joe's family. But just as all my children are created for a purpose, you too will understand your reason to be here. Many will love you, and in return you will be a great emotional healer, giving to others the love you hold in your heart. My intention is for all creation, human and animal, to be worthy of love, and treated with decency. Every life is meaningful—every life is vital."

Above all, let your love for one another be intense, because love covers a multitude of sins.
~ 1 Peter 4:8, NABRE

Affirmation: To heal one another is one of life's greatest gifts.

CHAPTER VIII

There is an appointed time for everything, and a time for every affair
under the heavens.
~ Ecclesiastes 3:1, NABRE

I love my new forever home. Everyone makes me feel welcome and loved. If that isn't a jackpot, the family is Italian—that equates to lots of tasty meals, cooked by Geralynn, and tons of kisses. I have to admit I miss neither my hunger pains nor the hard surfaces upon which I was forced to sleep. However, the thorn in my side keeps digging deeper into my flesh as the pain in my legs intensifies. Some days I can hardly stand, but I keep a strong upper lip. I do not want to be a source of anxiety for My Boy. My gut feeling tells me all is not right with him.

Words between me and Joe are insignificant; his nonverbal communications tell all. I notice when he sits quietly, he taps his foot without musical accompaniments. Other times his jaw is taut and seldom breaks into the warm smile that I love. Juggling a career and a family must be rather challenging. His schedule is just a mite short of nonstop, alternating between professional commitments and family obligations. Despite being pulled in many directions, My Boy always has time for me and my siblings, Spartacus (Sparty), Greta, and Rommel, who I have come to love and admire for their unique philosophies and life approaches. We are an interesting assortment, with diverse personalities, yet all the same. Kind of like people all created in God's image and likeness who differ in some aspects.

For in Christ Jesus you are all sons of God, through faith. For as many of you as were baptized into Christ have put on Christ. There is neither Jew nor Greek, there is neither slave nor free, there is no male and female, for you are all one in Christ Jesus.
~ Galatians 3:26–28, ESV

We communicate with looks, behavior, and body language. There is no Tower of Babel confusion among us. The trimmings matter not. In our hearts we offer unconditional love and loyalty. And unlike complicated humans who often create pure confusion and conflict with their relentless words, we hear and see beyond all the disturbing chaos of blaring echoes. However, I do have the impression from time to time that Joe wishes I could speak to him as Geralynn does.

Sparty is ever in command and very territorial. Lovingly he made me understand the importance of leadership even without expending a breath. One must always be in control to protect and defend others, to take the reins in hand. Intelligent as the human race is, sometimes they just cannot grasp the art of wordless dialogues, the ideal, proactive, and most operational means of communication.

Animals leave little if any room for error. Precise, effective, and explicit, animals leave nothing obstructed behind a barrier, whereas more often than not the spoken word generates misrepresentations and misconceptions. Sometimes I do notice a bit of dissension among my siblings.

There is no reason for concern—a master at conflict resolution, Sparty settles and calms the tides before any serious clashes escalate. Rommel and Greta, happy in their roles as loving, empathetic siblings, feel it is not worth the energy to combat for the five-star-general position.

Undeniably, Greta and Rommel accept their big brother's role as the patriarch of the canine branch of the family and respect his guidance. I am fine with Sparty as the helmsman, certain his seniority gives him the wisdom that makes him worthy.

"My child, I can see you are beginning to learn the ways of the earth and the differences among my creatures. Although as you know, everyone is equal in my eyes and was created as such, personalities and characters have varying degrees of shadings. The world needs variety, and I have obliged with an assortment of humans and animals. Nevertheless, my plan involves peaceful coexistence among my creatures, in harmony, loving and respecting each other while living dignified lives."

God's words make sense. Just because I am a pit bull, Sparty, Greta, and Rommel are dachshunds, and another dog down the street is a Doberman doesn't mean we are not deserving of the same love, respect, and freedom to live our lives. We are different only in physical appearance, but all equal in creation.

I like to cuddle and snuggle just as much as they do. At first, because of my size, I am hesitant, fearful I might be too heavy if I gain access to Joe or Geralynn's laps, but that passes within seconds as soon as their outstretched arms beckon me. Everyone thrives on love, and I am not an exception, though truthfully, I prefer to give it. "In every way, I have shown you that by hard work of that sort we must help the weak, and keep in mind the words of the Lord Jesus who himself said, 'It is more blessed to give than to receive'" (Acts 20:35, NABRE).

The pain persists. Restless, I am careful not to disturb my siblings. Sparty's reassuring snore leaves me at ease, likewise the steady rhythmic breathing of Greta and Rommel. How peacefully they sleep, unhindered by physical or emotional ills. Undoubtedly, Joe and Geralynn are blessed in their dreams.

Wakeful, I watch as darkness edges into light. It is a beautiful dawn, and after our morning prayer and breakfast, My Boy asks me to accompany him on a walk. In excruciating pain, I oblige, unwilling to let him down.

Please God, let me be able to handle this situation. I do not want to upset Joe. He seems to have deep concerns. But I will try my best to be a mediator in his life. Please don't let him notice my limping.

The more I step forward, the more piercing the agony. *Where are you, God? Why don't you help me? Have I offended you?*

"My child, I hear you and suffer for your distress. You have committed no wrong. However, I have my reasons for allowing this moment. You must trust in my will and in my timing. I know what is best."

He said to them, "It is not for you to know times or seasons that the
Father has fixed by his own authority."
~ Acts 1:7, ESV

"What's wrong, Shelby?" Joe asks, halting his steps. "It looks as if you are in pain," he adds, stooping to his knee to get a closer look. As he touches my left hind leg, a wince escapes, much as I try to muffle it. The aching is agonizing. A gradual head turn prohibits him from seeing my eyes, unable to conceal my feelings.

"Shelby, what's going on?" My Boy insists, a worried look swiping across his face. "Who did this to you? Who has so much hate and evil in their heart to torture a defenseless pup? It's criminal!"

He knows, God, he knows!

With the tip of his index finger, he gently pulls my face toward his. Quickly I steal a few licks to distract him, catching him right on the nose—no such luck. My Boy knows something is wrong. "Shelby, I'm going to phone the vet and set up an appointment."

The following day, Joe and I drive to a strange place. The antiseptic aroma hits my nostrils as we enter. Other dogs and a cat are seated. A woman behind the counter greets Joe with a wide, tooth-baring smile. I draw close to My Boy. Though apprehensive, I start to relax as he caresses my head. "It's going to be okay, Baby Girl," he whispers. I desperately want to swish my tongue across his cheek but fear it might embarrass him. My legs burn more intensely with every effort to sit quietly. When the shivering begins, I pray Joe will not notice. He does. But when I slump over, My Boy's heart breaks. He knows. He sees the red furless patches on my legs.

I have no way of knowing Joe's questioning mind, notwithstanding his restless, sleepless nights struggling to find a motive for my sadness. The Hollywood scene would never be my career choice. Not only am I incapable of acting, but my gold eyes betray me more often than not!

"Be at peace, my child, despite the challenges you will encounter. Do not worry; it will all work out. I have a plan for you once you are healed, but before you are ready to fulfill my wishes, you must pass through a period of strife and physical trials. Walk this moment beside me, and your heart and soul will be ready for your next chapter. Whether you lived or died has been entirely Joe's decision. Soon you will repay the favor."

Does God mean I will save My Boy? And from what? The following weekend I overhear Joe and Geralynn speaking softly in the kitchen. "The depression sometimes takes my breath away; it leaves me powerless," he says. "Sometimes I reflect on my condition, defining the indifference of depression as an alibi for dereliction of duty."

"Not necessarily, Joe," Geralynn responds. "In many cases, there are viable resources and management options, just like an ulcer or any malady, even though there is no guaranteed success rate. On the other hand, there are no unconditional assurances in life."

I stop breathing, unwilling to miss a word. Now I understand why My Boy is so sad at times and feels so lifeless. He suffers from depression, and it is not to be made light of, as it is an illness with potentially serious consequences. I hope he is seeing a therapist and following a course of treatment. I resolve to remain close to Joe and pray for his healing.

Today is a gloomy, dark, rainy day. Geralynn, Joe, and Jenna are at work and in school. My Boy is sitting in his office. His eyes are closed, though his tapping foot assures he is not asleep.

"I'm losing it," he whispers several times. His words are barely audible. "Everything is hopeless—only misery and despair haunt me. The daily stress factors like ravenous weeds in a fruitful garden. It closes in a bit tighter every day, overpowering, depleting my life force with its assailing stampede, regenerating the PTSD of years and past circumstances, until now, predominantly incognito, under the sod. This is not how God intended my life, nor as I care to exist. I cannot continue my . . ."

What is Joe saying? He cannot continue what? I am confused, and it disturbs me. I have never seen My Boy so downtrodden. *God, please help!*

My Boy suddenly rises from his chair. I watch without being seen. He walks to the bedroom. I trail in his footsteps, still an invisible force. From the doorway, I see he reaches for a container of pills—his medication. Something is very wrong. I feel pressure on my neck. I turn slowly but see no one. *Is that you, God?*

"Yes, my child, it is me. Your time has come. Do not worry; I will give you the strength."

"Shelby, where are you?" My Boy calls, unexpectedly. I step out of the shadows, standing in full view. Tears are rolling down his cheeks. My stomach churns. I follow him to the living room. He turns and drops to his knees, the container of pills firmly secured in his clasped fist. We are eye to eye: the heart-to-heart confrontation.

"Now, my child, *now*! It's your turn."

He folds one hand on top of another, palms up, and slides them under my chin. He's trembling. My heart is breaking. I stand strong, though my legs are about to collapse. My Boy leans forward and kisses my nose. I gather all the love in my heart and channel it directly into his eyes, certain he will not be able to resist my energy. *I know, Joe, life hurts. But love, empathy, and compassion calm the pain. You have given and continue to give it to me, and now I am here to give it to you.*

"How can I leave you, my sweet Baby Girl," Joe sobs. "You were abandoned once, and you will never survive another desertion, another betrayal, another cruelty. It cannot happen again."

Quickly I free my face from his cradling hands and cover his salty, tear-stained face with sticky licks. Sticky, because he must never forget them. When I get to his ear, I make sure he understands we are soul mates, hand-selected by God in this life at this precise moment. This is why our paths have crossed. We are in this together. My paw weighs heavily on his hand. The pills drop on the carpet. Simultaneously our breaths echo in unison: Sighs of solace, of release? Does it really matter?

God, I believe I have fulfilled my purpose in saving Joe. Does this mean I have to leave him and return to you? God, I don't want to leave him.

"My child, you have served a wonderful purpose today, but your mission is far from complete. You have a long path ahead and many thresholds to cross."

Thank you, God. My tail wags in large, sweeping circles. I have now tasted happiness: such a precious honied delicacy.

Each of you should use whatever gift you have received to serve others, as faithful stewards of God's grace in its various forms.
~ 1 Peter 4:10, NIV

Affirmation: Humans need to be rescued and assisted during hard times just as much as animals do.

CHAPTER IX

*Put on then, as God's chosen ones, holy and beloved, heartfelt
compassion, kindness, humility, gentleness, and patience, bearing with
one another and forgiving one another, if one has a grievance against
another; as the Lord has forgiven you, so must you also do.*

~ Colossians 3:12–13, NABRE

I know my acquittal from famine and brutality, nonetheless a necessary
rite of passage, is indeed a precious blessing for which, God willing, I
intend to give back. Through all the tribulations I have endured during
my brief time on earth, through my loss of puppyhood innocence, I have
learned that God and Joe are my lifelines; therefore both have earned my
unwavering trust.

I have faith, but I continue to pray, always fearful of my legs. Over
time, the pain is worsening. Meanwhile, Joe has a conference with the vet
to clarify and discuss solutions for the damage to my hind limbs. I am no
longer able to join Rommel, Sparty, and Greta nestled beside My Boy on
the sofa, unassisted. I try not to trigger undue concern or disappoint Joe
during our walks.

**"My child, through you I saved Joe; now it's his turn to save you
from your agony. Then together you will rescue others from their
inner demons. Do you understand now the importance of your life?
Perhaps it's premature, but you will soon enough."**

My gaze meets Joe's. His eyes are radiant.

"My dear Shelby, the time has come to unbolt the weighty shackles of your tormented past, remembering the feelings of anguish, forgiving those who have offended me in the wickedness of sin, and prepare for a new springtime, based on the strengths and perspectives acquired as a result of your personal experience with tribulations and salvation.

"It's a time of regeneration in the fulfillment of my plan. It debuted the evening you rescued Joe from the potentially fatalistic consequences a deeply troubled mind can generate. Soon, to you will be unveiled your earthly purpose. Go forth, my beautiful child, and carry out my mission on earth. Joe, too, is my emissary. Let him be your guide. It is my will. And now let him be your comfort in suffering."

The pain in my legs is now relentless and almost impossible to conceal from Joe. He knows I am ailing but is unable to access the extent of my injuries or the intensity of my suffering. Only my muted agony and the MRI betray the secret—or so I think.

"Baby Girl," Joe calls, a worried look crossing his face. As always, I scamper over to him, giving a few licks to his outstretched hands. "I have some good news and some not-so-good news," he continues. The defining moment—his eyes in direct synchrony with mine.

Immediately I know it has to be about my legs, also because I overheard him speaking on the phone with the vet. If a doctor can fix my problem, I will be grateful. The pain is exhausting, and My Boy will do the best to heal my injuries. I have to admit, butterflies are crossing paths in my stomach.

"Shelby, tomorrow morning we are going to meet with one of the best surgeons here in the area. Unfortunately, your legs are seriously maimed. You will require a more in-depth evaluation and probably surgery. On the positive side, however, following the surgical repair, you will be able to walk again without grimacing agony."

Straightforward and honest, I know it's torturous for him to vocalize these words, but Joe never shies away from the truth, even if painful.

I trust My Boy; therefore, whatever he decides is best, I accept. *Please, God, just don't let me disappoint Joe. Also, please give me the strength to overcome all that you send me.*

"My child, to suffer is to embrace the divine purpose, the humbling sacrifice for salvation. Under the wing of pain awaits redemption— from misery stems a strengthening of your relationship with me, though perhaps in confusion. Some decisions of mine will not enable understanding, but the glory resides in blind faith acceptance and the unconditional embracing of my will."

Once again, I don't quite understand the full meaning of God's message, but I grasp His wish for absolute compliance and realize through the endurance and bearing of pain, I will be nourished and fortified with special gifts. The following morning after breakfast and a quick walk for my necessities, Geralynn gives me a big hug. "It's going to be all good in the end, Shelby," she assures. "I'll be praying for you."

Joe helps me into the car. His furrowed brow relaxes when I fix my gaze on him. I will never show him any hesitation for fear of upsetting him. When we arrive at the Animal Emergency and Referral Associates in Fairfield, I try to steady my tremor. God is with me. A kind, slight-of-stature woman dressed in blue scrubs quickly escorts us to a visiting room.

The meeting with the surgeon is uncomfortable with his fingers probing my legs. Diligently he scrutinizes the results of my lab and radiology tests. "Joe, I see that Shelby's vet has made some recommendations. At this point, I agree with his diagnosis. There is no doubting Shelby has bilateral cranial cruciate ligament ruptures. She will need extensive surgical repairs."

I know My Boy tortures himself, trying to find answers for my injuries. He tries to breathe deeply, slowly. The vet's words pierce his heart like a dagger dipped in poison. An animal-loving guy, he will never understand why some callous individuals hurt us, though we are innocent and defenseless creatures just seeking to give love.

Joe is aware of the traumatic status of my mutilated legs. God and I have made a pact to keep the origins of my wounds under a question mark, though he knows it was wicked violence. And convinced I was badly abused, he vows to give his life to stop animal brutality and savagery. Nothing will ever free him from the unknowns in my life—why his Baby Girl was abandoned, starved, crippled, and fastened to a fence in a gas station on a cold, damp evening under the pouring rain.

I feel anxious and unsure of what surgery means. Nonetheless, I will pray as My Boy taught me. I know he is together with God for my healing.

Do not fear: I am with you; do not be anxious: I am your God. I will strengthen you, I will help you, I will uphold you with my victorious right hand.
~ Isaiah 41:10, NABRE

"My child, I brought you here on earth. I will always stand by you. Be not weary or filled with fear. The weak and the fragile have my support to triumph. But to overcome, you must be committed to your purpose here on earth. In your reason to be rests the strength to heal and eventually forgive those who have caused such injury in a young, innocent pup.

"Many fail to realize that all my creatures have a heart and a soul. Every one of them, from a tiny insect dragging along the ground searching for a crack to build a nest, to an elephant enjoying mastery,

weighing as much as ten thousand pounds, suffers when mistreated. I did not make animals for entertainment or financial gain. I made them to enjoy life; therefore, any contradiction or rebellion disturbing my plan is a grave sin, a crime against the sacred nature of life."

"Joe," the surgeon begins, clearing his throat, "don't look so devastated. The good news is that I can help Shelby and alleviate her pain. The surgery will stabilize her legs, improve her strength and endurance, and slow the rapid progression of osteoarthritis. Her prognosis is excellent!"

My Boy's face lights up in a big smile as he exhales heavily. I wag my tail to show him I am happy. *Thank you, God. Please never let me disappoint Joe.*

The tibial plateau leveling osteotomy (TPLO) restorative surgery is scheduled, and we head home. In the car, My Boy rests his head on the steering wheel. From the slight tremor of his body, I know he is overwhelmingly distraught.

The thought of the surgery ordeal breaks his heart even though it is warranted to mend the ruptured ligaments and increase my range of motion. As he pulls away from the curb, I lean forward from my back seat and lick his bald head. I know it's dangerous to touch someone while behind the wheel, but God is with us. Joe and I understand each other. Sometimes our hearts beat as one. It is how the Creator intended.

Affirmation: When you need to stay strong during adversity, thank God for the strength, and pray for the firmness and resistance to assist and support others.

CHAPTER X

Come to me, all you who are weary and burdened,
and I will give you rest.
~ Matthew 11:28, NIV

Several days later, My Boy calls me, Sparty, Greta, and Rommel and speaks to us about my surgery within a few hours. He reassures my siblings: "Shelby will have to endure some pain and be uncomfortable for a while, but once her convalescence and healing are completed, she will be able to run and play with you. We will pray this morning for her quick recovery." My eyes are tearing. One by one my siblings walk over to me. Licking the tip of my nose, each one offers love, compassion, and well wishes, fully aware of the ordeal I am about to undergo. Though deeply concerned, they reassure me of their love and support.

"My child, have no worries or concerns. Everything will unravel as it was designed in my plan. You will demonstrate to doubters and disbelievers that my animal creations feel pain, love, and empathy for others. They comfort the afflicted and give love to all."

I try to remain calm for My Boy, but I am scared. Joe needs me, and I don't want to leave him. Inside I am melting like a crystalline icicle trapped in direct sunlight. Its illuminating spike expands under the incessant drip of water, assuming the guise of a waterfall frozen in time. I must stay strong.

Christianity is about repentance. God has a sense of humor. For sure the next few weeks will be sacrificial. I am willing. Geralynn volunteered last evening to drive us to the Animal Emergency and Referral Associates.

This kindness leaves my boy relieved, though he is a man true to his faith commitments and trusting in the mercy of God. The ride is smooth. Silence prevails. Once there, the staff welcomes us with full-tooth smiles, treating me as a VID, a very important dog. Joe is thrilled and seems more relaxed.

Notwithstanding my red-carpet treatment, at the parting moment, I fix my eyes on Joe as the assistant reaches for my leash—a torturous lingering gaze, though wrapped in love. What if I never see Joe again? What if I don't make it?

"My child, remember—never lose faith, regardless of how discouraged you may be. I am with you always."

It's time for the surgical preparations. As I wag my tail to let Joe know I'm ready, he dissolves into uncontrollable tears. Our bond is unimaginable.

"My child, Joe tried his best to keep it together, but you have to understand, the consequences of human wickedness toward innocent animals are just too overwhelming for a man like him to endure. I will give him extra strength today as I entrust you to the surgeon with a special blessing."

How fortunate I am. God loves me, Joe loves me, and my family loves me. I am beginning to see some merit in my agonizing early months of life. My thoughts are interrupted: the assistant is shaving my legs. Thankfully I do not have to do this often like human women. Regardless, my legs looked better before the shave! I do not want My Boy to see me like this.

"Relax, Shelby," the surgeon whispers. I am being anesthetized. My last conscious thought is a prayer begging God to return me safely to Joe: prayer answered. According to the vet, the surgery outcome is excellent; thus, as a young pup, I should be up and running in due time. One night in recovery and I am back in the car with Joe driving us home. Happy, though in excruciating pain, I give thanks.

Joe is informed that my recovery will take about four months. I am more than in discomfort, confined in a cone-shaped lamp shade contraption. It's called the Elizabethan collar, and My Boy tells me to be patient. "Baby Girl," he whispers, "you must wear the collar for a while. I know it is uncomfortable, but it is designed to prevent you from licking, gnawing at, or scratching your sutures."

I am trying to behave—for Joe. I think he is suffering more than I am. Sometimes it hurts more to see a loved one suffer. He knows the cause, and that increases the intensity of his anguish. This morning I swallowed my medication, though not before licking my boy's fingers as he placed it on my tongue. The smile on his face trumps all my agony.

"Shelby, I know you are in pain, but walking is important to ward off skin deterioration and the possibility of bedsores," my loving nurse Joe says. How blessed I am. From an abused abandoned pup, I am living in the arms of unconditional love and nurturing. My every need is gratified without even asking. Joe is exceptionally conscientious and meticulous with my wound care, meals, and vitamins. God is truly loving. If only everyone could find a place in their heart to love animals as Joe does.

"My child, the worst is over. You have had to learn my ways. Sometimes people cry and shout that I am not a just God, turning against me, questioning why I allow pain. What they fail to understand is that man offended me, trying to contradict my wishes in the Garden of Eden. This led to a loss of paradise and the start of earthly existence with suffering and hardships, though always pardoned if forgiveness is implored."

The Son of Man will send his angels, and they will collect out of his kingdom all who cause others to sin and all evildoers. They will throw

them into the fiery furnace, where there will be wailing and grinding of
teeth.
~ Matthew 13:41–42, NABRE

**"My child, you are grinding your teeth in pain, as Jesus did on
the cross. The anguish will make you a truly compassionate being
and instill in you a special feeling. You will treat others with empathy.
Here lies the groundwork for your mission—a mission of service to
others, but not without first learning the meaning of suffering. Never
let a tear, anxiety, or pain fall by the wayside. Gather the frailties of
life, and I will help you turn them into beautiful deeds. The greater
the suffering, the more God-like you are."**

God has given me much to reflect upon. I will not disappoint Him. I
know Joe will support and assist me. This is God's will. I will obey.

Affirmation: Never waver through adversity; instead, take inspiration
for your mission from the challenge before you.

CHAPTER XI

Bear one another's burdens, and so you will fulfill the law of Christ.
~ Galatians 6:2, NABRE

My convalescence is a bittersweet life experience. On one hand, the pain is severe and rotates between stabbing and pulsating. On the other hand, the love, compassion, and nurturing I am receiving from Joe, Geralynn, and Jenna are far more efficacious in pain management and healing than any medication or treatment. I am trying to focus on getting better, though often the exercise therapy has me screaming in silence not to disturb My Boy. But when he cradles me in his arms, I feel safe, protected from all the past hurts. And when I nuzzle him, my pain lessens. The power of love. How wonderful it must be to comfort others.

"My child, when I see my creatures ministering to others, it brings joy to my heart. It truly speaks of living in my heartbeats and following in my footsteps. It makes me happy to hear you say it must be wonderful to comfort others. And you shall do so. This is the meaning of your life and the core of your mission."

I love God. I pray, always asking Him to bless my family. Though strong in faith, sometimes I do not understand His words. He speaks about my mission, words that have me baffled. But as God has taught me—all in due time!

"Shelby, it's such a cool autumn evening, how about accompanying me and Geralynn to the park for some ice cream?" My tail breaks into a rhythmic sway—my way of assuring Joe I will be delighted. Within minutes Geralynn slips the collar around my neck. Thrilled to be invited for ice cream, I pray my acceptance will not disappoint. If only my legs will not hurt so badly.

Please, God, I will bear the pain as is your wish; just don't let me upset My Boy. He's been having some difficulties with his depression, and I want my presence here to be of assistance.

"My child, I ask you always to trust me, and now I ask you to trust Joe. You have settled in nicely with Geralynn, Joe, and Jenna, but you must begin to feel comfortable with humans outside your family. You are not alone in suffering. It is part of the earthly condition. Many of my creatures feel lonely, defenseless, and hopeless, just as you did before Joe rescued you. Many live with terrible pains. Do you ever think that maybe you can rescue others?"

I do not know what God intends for me. How can I rescue anyone? My heart is throbbing. I have to find out what is expected of me. I know my reprieve from the arrows of wickedness is truly a special blessing.

"Shelby, my child. I have asked you to have faith and trust me. Never doubt my word. And remember—always be patient. Now enjoy your walk with Joe and Geralynn, and pay attention to your surroundings. The answer will come."

Gently, Joe lifts me into the car and shuts the door. He walks a few steps to make certain Geralynn is safely in the passenger seat. Caring for others is so typical of My Boy. Sliding behind the wheel, we take off. Little do I know this will be a new beginning in the unraveling of God's plan.

Within a quarter hour, we pull up along the curb of a park filled with laughing children, Frisbee-chasing dogs, and people of all ages engaged in conversations or listening to music through their Airpods and just enjoying the gifts of God—the beauty of nature at no cost to anyone.

"How are you feeling, Baby Girl?" My Boy asks, concerned about my limping. I rub my moist nose against the back of his hand and wag my tail. He understands that I am willing to walk.

I notice a gentleman of advanced age, seated in a wheelchair under a large oak tree. He looks forlorn, probably as I did when rescued at the gas station. Maybe he would welcome some love and attention. I certainly would have that cold rainy evening. The plight of loneliness crosses his face from time to time while he watches life around him as a spectator from outside the circle.

"It's your turn, My child."

An impossible-to-curtail urge changes my direction as I head over to the gentleman. My Boy feels the pull on the leash and follows my lead, though I feel his mounting apprehension. "Shelby, what's happening?" A response is unnecessary.

"Hello, Shelby," the gentleman calls, catching sight of me and approaching. He overhears Joe address me by name. Extending his arms in an inviting gesture, I inch close enough for him to caress me. "You're so beautiful and so very sweet," he compliments, trying to conceal sadness behind a smile, years of sadness dulled.

I turn toward Joe and Geralynn for approval. They are smiling, their eyes welling with tears.

"She's going right up to him," My Boy blurts, excited. Withdrawing her breath, Geralynn remains silent, her gaze inquisitive. Soon questions will be answered.

I like this kind gentleman, but he has a melancholy heart. I feel his pain. I want to help him, at least let him know someone cares—me. I care. *God, please don't let me frighten him.*

"My child, never let fear be an impediment. Be who you are—who I created you to be."

I ask God for assistance and strength and take the liberty of placing my head on the gentleman's lap, praying I can share with him some of the comforting moments I enjoy with My Boy.

"Geralynn, are you seeing what I'm seeing?" Joe is stunned. "Unbelievable! She should be fearful, mistrusting of humans for how they tortured her, yet . . ."

"Yes, Joe, this is the hand of God directing Shelby."

"I think God is directing me also, leading me along a diverse path with Shelby. I knew she was different, but this proves she is a very special dog."

My Boy is reading my thoughts. Tears meander down his cheeks. In the language of silence, he offers solidarity and approval. Quickly I gaze up at my new gentleman friend. From ashen to rosy, his complexion colors, gradually taking on a luminescent glow. Eyes shaded behind memories of forfeited privileges mixed with the almost forgotten freedom of independence well up with a return to joy. Am I responsible for this?

For a brief interlude, I feel neither my painful legs nor the intermittent heaviness in my heart. Instead, I feel a new warmth where coldness once invaded, a more gratifying satisfaction than a full stomach after weeks of starvation. I feel a certain lightness of being—can it possibly be happiness? Perhaps I have brought a smile to the divine face.

"My child, you have followed in my footsteps—understood my message. You offered compassion; you came when someone was ill and imprisoned in loneliness."

I was naked and you clothed me, I was sick and you visited me, I was in prison and you came to me.

~ Matthew 25:36, ESV

God has given me empathy and compassion; now I must give the gifts to others. I feel a new spurt of life. Something beautiful is happening within me. I have just come face-to-face with who I am!

The drive home is quiet but rich in lessons, messages, and the vitality of a new awareness: an epiphany moment. It is uplifting to show a little compassion to those in pain. If I can make someone forget their ills, be they physical, emotional, or psychological, even for five minutes, I will have stepped into my purpose—the reason God has brought me here, merged my path and entwined my life with Joe's. As the beneficiary of love and nurturing, I have a mission, a vocation to give back. Gradually the fog lifts, the clouds shift, and the road before me clears. I am here to assist and empower all whom God sets before me. Neither heroic nor exceptional, this unthreaded trail blazed by God is open to all.

"Geralynn, today my Baby Girl made the life of a lonely man on the final lap of his journey brighter and more worthwhile. He received love—he learned amid his doubts that someone does understand and cares, be it a four-pawed Samaritan."

As My Boy leans over to plant a kiss on my face, our intentions unite. Unexpectedly, I swipe the tip of my nose across his bald head. My tongue exits. Sometimes it is impossible not to kiss Joe.

"Shelby, you and I have a joined destiny! Are you my tail-wagging angel?"

Hearing my words, Geralynn smiles, caressing my arm. "Joe, sometimes God passes over the human race when selecting His messengers."

"Yes, maybe it depends on who can do the job better," My Boy responds. My two favorite people enjoy a hug and a slight giggle. Delighted, I experience another rush of happiness.

"Geralynn," Joe begins, settling in his preferred chair, "wasn't that amazing? It was so inspiring. Would you ever have expected such nurturing from a pup, an abused, beaten pup? Despite her young age, she seemed to connect with the man's suffering and thirst for compassion. She seemed to relate to him instantaneously—it was all so unplanned, instinctive! Didn't it seem like two people finding and sharing a commonality between them?

"I think Shelby is a therapy dog in the making. Maybe this is the meaning behind her journey of suffering. Perhaps this is why she was born and why she came to live with us."

I do not understand the significance of Joe and Geralynn's conversation, though I feel they are pleased with me.

"My child, you are a compassionate, loving soul. Joe and Geralynn have seen the magnetism of your empathy. Soon many will come to learn some amazing life lessons from you and understand how much they can acquire from the beloved animals I created."

"Sweet Shelb of mine," I hear My Boy singing. Nice to know he is feeling uplifted today. When he sees my inquisitive look, he clears his throat. I know something important is coming, so I settle down as gracefully as I can, considering I am not yet 100% healed.

"Shelby, all life, including your suffering and mine, is part of God's plan. Watching you administer love to that elderly gentleman under the oak tree is a strong message. I rescued you and, in return, you saved me from my worst enemy—myself trapped in a suffocating depression. We both stood on the edge while the winds of life were kicking up. I must give back to God—no, we must give back to God, and I will help you grow into who you were created to be. Shelby, my beautiful Baby Girl, you are a soother, a comforter in times of distress; you are a therapy dog. Your heart is brimming over with love and compassion for others."

Affirmation: It is possible to lighten the burden of another: Do not miss an opportunity to comfort, empower, and encourage.

CHAPTER XII

But I say to you, love your enemies, and pray for those who persecute
you, that you may be children of your heavenly Father, for he makes
his sun rise on the bad and the good, and causes rain to fall on the just
and the unjust.

~ Matthew 5:44–45, NABRE

"My child, the time has come. You are ready to fulfill your purpose.
Your spirit is sensitive to the meaning of suffering and open to the
pains of others."

God knows me. I now understand His words. It is true. When I see
people hurting, my heart wells up with love. I have a strong urge to go to
them. Sometimes fear impedes me. I have to overcome my struggles with
the past. Sadly, it happened, but perhaps as a result, my presence today can
make the sick and troubled feel loved, as Joe does with me. It works. A little
bit of caring distracts from the wounds of aggravated trauma and turmoil.

"Baby Girl, I think you will feel fulfilled as a therapy dog. You are
loyal and faithful. You listen for hours when I ramble about my issues; you
never once have contradicted me or passed judgment on anything I have
told you. You're a psychologist, a four-pawed Florence Nightingale, and a
pardoning confidante without a confessional. Would you be interested in
pursuing?" My Boy asks.

With a sweeping motion of my tail, Joe has the answer. A beaming,
approving smile brightens his face. "I will wait until your legs heal, then I
will take you to Bright and Beautiful Therapy Dogs to be evaluated, tested,

71

and trained for the certification. They are nonprofit and specialize in teaching dogs like you, my sweet Baby Girl—dogs given the gift of charisma. They will prepare you to carry out God's plan for your purpose to succor men, women, and children of all ages and ethnicities, even individuals at death's door—people psychologically struggling with various levels of disabilities, chronic conditions, and handicaps, as well as those grieving the loss of a dearly beloved."

Who, me? I can do all that? I am a bit intimidated by Joe's words. He certainly thinks highly of me. What if I fail the test? What if I disappoint both God and Joe? It sounds complicated. As if reading my thoughts, Joe reassures, "You will do brilliantly, Shelby; don't be intimidated by the incidentals."

Incidentals? Evaluation and testing? My Boy has a sense of humor at times.

"My beautiful Baby Girl, you are a charismatic soul with an expansive nurturing character, a calm, sometimes stoic personality, and above all a heart so full of love I often fear it will burst. Once they meet you, there will be no denying the inevitable. You are an angel of mercy born to move grimaces into smiles and halt the overflow of tears. Do not worry about the test; I will help you." I say nothing but keep my fear concealed in silence, under my wagging tail.

"My child, you are wandering in faith. Remember my words. Always do your best, and never walk away from me. My hand will never leave your shoulders. Only the doubters fail, those of little faith."

God has placed a big challenge on my shoulders. However, if He selected me for a special ministry, He must think I am worthy. God is unerring.

Approaching My Boy, I give his fingers a few licks. He loves when I do it.

"Don't worry, Shelb, I'm here for you." As always, Joe never strays from his word. "I will give you a preliminary test to see your level of obedience." Wagging my tail, My Boy understands I am ready. I *sit* when he asks me to, I *stand*, I *halt*, and I *heel* to gratify his wishes. "Great! Next stop, the therapy dog test." Our eyes meet as I wag my tail in appreciation. "You're a gracious lady, Shelby." I blush.

Joe works diligently with me to prepare for my test. Jenna creates disturbing noises to distract me, but I do not waver. "Excellent," My Boy says, patting me on the head, "you will do just fine." While waiting for the appointment, I learn to walk past a treat placed on the floor without retrieving it unless or until given the okay to pick it up. This is easy. Learning tolerance in the light of clumsy, rough, and repetitive irritating petting and suffocating hugs requires God's help as well as retaining a serene demeanor through the turbulence of elevated vocal communications.

"My child, you will do brilliantly. You will make Joe proud."

God has spoken the magic words. I live for My Boy. *God, my test is on Sunday. I'm counting on you.*

"My sweet angel, faith opens doors."

Today is my test. I think Joe is more nervous than I am. God is with me. I will do it.

"Shelby," the man conducting the evaluation calls, "it's your turn." Joe and I exchange loving glances. With my tail, I swat his calf. There is no way I will disappoint either God or Joe. And I don't. When you set an intention, fight distractions, and focus on succeeding—you will not fail. Centered on the task at hand, I perform every exercise and heed every command with meticulous precision. One challenge remains—deciphering if I have the composure skill. I will be perfect. The test coordinator tugs at my ear several times. Stoic, I stand motionless, pretending nothing is happening.

So do not fear, for I am with you.
~ Isaiah 41:10, NIV

"Excellent, Shelby," he shouts, patting me on the head. "You will make a great therapy dog." My heart is thumping. My eyes are glued on My Boy as he runs deliriously with joy to smother me with kisses. Thus begins my career as a therapy dog. I am about to embrace my reason to be—my purpose here on earth, besides taking care of Joe. *Thank you, God—your will be done!*

I have overcome several hurdles, but will I be able to conquer the memory of those men who hurt me so badly? Can I trust anyone besides Joe and his family? And what if it happens again? "Father, forgive them, they know not what they do" (Luke 23:34, NABRE).

"My child, forgive those who have done you wrong—those without kindness in their hearts, those who live hurting my creatures—humans and animals. Every living being deserves respect, dignity, and the right to a serene life in quest of happiness.

"Give thanks for your sweet heart that knows nothing but love. Many will learn from your goodness, many will be comforted, and many will follow your ways. Always be kind to all, especially those who seem troubled and walk never with a smile or a hand clasped in another. Some of my creatures are carrying heavy burdens. Just be patient, tolerant, and above all forgiving for all those who in ignorance have trespassed against you. You have my blessing to carry out your beautiful ministry. Share with others the gifts I have given you."

*Go, therefore, and make disciples of all nations, baptizing them in the name of the Father, and of the Son, and of the Holy Spirit . . .
And behold, I am with you always, until the end of the age.*
~ Matthew 28:19–20, NABRE

I know it breaks Joe's heart to tell me that I have to face more surgery on my legs. "But this will make you all better, my sweet Shelb." Man becomes like the Son of God when he embraces suffering; therefore, I will not disillusion anyone with my misery even if my pain is excruciating. The appointment has been scheduled and, like a soldier, I march, optimistic and with God's shared strength of endurance and acceptance. In the end, I not only survive, I thrive. Moreover, I have intense compassion for all who suffer.

God has blessed my faith with a full recovery. Remaining on my inner thighs, the deep scars attesting to my trip to hell are, according to Joe, "a lasting testimony of my crucifixion and determination to rise again." Now I want to let go, surrender my life to God's will, and be His emissary on four paws.

When Easter Seals calls for me, Joe somersaults, metaphorically speaking, so overpowering is his elation. "Shelby, this is a nonprofit assisting adults with developmental issues, handicapped, special-needs children and teens, and those dealing with psychological problems. What an honor, Baby Girl!"

The following morning, in a calmer mode, he reaches in his desk drawer and pulls out a red bandana and the TDI tag—my therapy dog badge and uniform. I cannot tell who is more excited, me or My Boy, but the adrenaline of joy is sprouting like an open New York fire hydrant.

Today is June 9, 2009, the moment I step into who I am. Off we go, Joe and me, side by side to the Easter Seals facility in New Rochelle. Upon entry, several people reach out to touch me. One young man encircles his arms around my waist, squeezing me in a bear hug. Slowly I place myself on the tile floor to make it easier to embrace or pet me. I am caught off guard when an elderly gentleman cradles my head in heavily calloused palms. What an initiation ceremony! With barely a few seconds to catch my breath, a twenty-something girl on all fours caresses my back with her face.

"How are you doing, Shelby?" Joe asks, somewhat anxious. "Everyone is so relaxed around you. It seems as if you have erased their disabilities and canceled their sadness from defining who they are." My tail wags, telling him I am joyful doing God's work. Happiness is sharing and giving the happiness gift to others.

"Baby Girl," My Boy begins on the way home, "to witness firsthand scowls flip into smiles and tears evaporate before my eyes as individuals hampered by physical and emotional limitations shed their melancholy for a few minutes is fulfilling. Did you notice how they clung to you like magnets searching for stability? You have no idea what you have done for me today—you have removed me from a dark cloud behind the rainbow and placed me directly on the arc in full sunlight."

Am I worthy of such praise?

"Yes, my child, and you are just taking your first steps. Many will walk with an easy gait and a lifted spirit in your presence. Perhaps now you are beginning to understand why you were tortured, abused, and neglected. My gift of free will to man is responsible, but all for a purpose. Only after having experienced anguishing pain are you capable of realizing the meaning and intensity of earthly suffering."

Frequently Joe would tell my story of abandonment and rescue to various staff members at the different facilities we visited daily—hospitals, schools, and organizations. The response is always the same: "Who would cast off, abuse, and neglect such an amazing, loving, and beautiful dog? She's an angel." God alone holds the answer in His heart.

My ministry of mercy takes me to hospitals to visit children and adults of all ages, those in anticipation of healing, and those waiting to greet their Creator. Each welcomes me when I climb into their beds, placing my head over their hearts and asking God to assist them during their difficult journey. I whisper to them, *I know your pain and feel it. Maybe I can make you forget for just a few minutes. If you don't mind, I will kiss you.* Who rejects love? No one ever does.

The dusk arrives, not necessarily with a promise for a radiant dawn, and I have learned that sometimes rain bursts forth from clouds warmed from the rays of the sun. Occasionally the contradictions in nature are forerunners of unexpected turbulence, just as joy can impulsively wander into melancholy.

When the New Jersey Township Family Service Bureau, after interviewing me, votes to have me serve as their therapy dog, to visit shut-ins, schools, and assisted living facilities, My Boy is thrilled. Then, with an ear-shattering clap of thunder, the tempest erupts.

The phone rings, and My Boy runs to respond. The caller is on speaker.

"Mr. Dwyer, I'm from the New Jersey Township Family Service Bureau," a high-pitched female voice announces. "I'm sorry to have to make this phone call, but once the board discovered Shelby is a pit bull, they made a special request for another vote." Nervously clearing her throat, she continues, "Unfortunately, the favorable decision has been reversed. Pit bulls are categorized as vicious—they have a reputation for violent behavior. I'm sorry, but we cannot assume the risk of engaging a ferocious dog; the liability would be overpowering. I'm certain you understand our reasoning for this decision."

My Boy pales, all color disappearing from his face. His breathing quickens as he slumps down in his chair, placing his head in his open palms. Anticipating his anxiety, I run to him, placing my face on his knee. I know it comforts him. Enraged by the prejudicial breed profiling, he tries to understand the reasoning, but ignorance has neither logic nor rationale. God has taught us to love and accept all creatures.

"This is unfair, Baby Girl," Joe whispers, visibly upset. "We will go to schools and teach the children about the toxic effects of bias and bullying. It is merciless discrimination."

I know how Joe feels. If people would take the time to become acquainted with diversity, they would see it truly exists only in the minds and hearts of the unknowledgeable. Ignorance contorts and warps the truth in the minds of those who wallow in it, but like the Son of God, I forgive them and pray they will come to see their errant thinking.

Nothing suffocates passion. Together with My Boy, I visit hospitals, nursing facilities, and schools. I love the children, and they await my arrival with the fresh enthusiasm of youth and innocence. They learn my story and come to understand the harmful consequences of bullying, the loss of self-esteem, the rise of feelings of inferiority with blooms of lost ambition.

No one has the right to diminish another. We all have special gifts and talents and a surplus of love to give. Why turn affection, respect, and admiration for God's creatures into hate and violence? It was done to the Son of God; it was done to Joe, and it was done to me. Let's break the cycle!

Affirmation: Never, ever judge or falsely profile anyone—man, woman, or animal.

CHAPTER XIII

Do not neglect to do good and to share what you have, for such
sacrifices are pleasing to God.
~ Hebrews 13:16, ESV

**"My child, be neither discouraged nor hurt by the bias demonstrated
at the New Jersey Township Family Bureau. Never forget that at the
base of prejudice is ignorance. For this reason, we cannot hold rancor
against those who dwell in darkness. Instead of feeling downtrodden
or chastising in exchange for aggression try to change misconceptions.
Joe is on the path and will need you by his side."**

I live for My Boy. Many years before I was born, I longed to be with
him. His wishes and dreams are my wishes and dreams. Often, he speaks
about my healing ministry. I am always ready to comfort the sick and
ailing. This morning as I sit near the window trying to catch a ray of sun
on my legs, I hear him in prayer.

"God, thank you for Shelby's successful surgery. Please let her heal
without undue agony. She has suffered sufficiently, and now it is time for
her to comfort others in pain. Let her learn to forgive and seek to produce
smiles instead of tears on the faces of others. This, above all, will give
Shelby closure and free her from her torturous past. Only then will she
understand her true value, the inestimable self-worth snatched from her
by evildoers together with the illiteracy of discrimination. And, with your
intervention, please let me guide her along the paths of her ministry, even
if not always obstacle-free."

Deeply moved, I continue to ask God to give me the strength not to disappoint.

"Baby Girl, tomorrow we're going to visit some patients at the Hackensack University Medical Center." Joe's words thrill me. Not only will I have a chance to comfort the ailing in one of the top-ten best hospitals for cardiac, cancer, and pediatrics, among other specialties, but I'll be spending the day with my favorite human. As always, my ventilating tail wags convey my joy.

The following day cannot dawn soon enough. After prayers and breakfast, I climb into the car, noticing the pain in my legs is less intense. Joe drives to the hospital, extending his arm periodically to pat my head in reassurance, though I am certain more in love.

It's a beautiful morning, a true blessing. As we pull into the parking area, I notice another vehicle. Suddenly the door opens and out steps a nicely dressed elderly woman with hair the color of snow. Her eyes meet mine, encouraging her to take several unsteadied steps defying her companion's cautionary warnings to wait for her to get over to the passenger side.

"I was just locking the doors; why didn't you wait for me, Mom?" the daughter admonishes softly. "You could lose your balance; you're trembling. Let's go inside."

"Just a moment," she interrupts emphatically. "I want to meet this dog." The vigor previously dormant in her body suddenly reanimates in her voice and her determination. My Boy approaches the woman, his chest swelling with pride. My tail wags in joy. I live for these instances to see Joe fill with happiness and witness strangers experience even a few fleeting moments of enjoyment.

While the elderly woman stands smiling at me, Joe cuts through the magnetic encounter. "Madam, would you like to meet her?" he questions, gesturing in my direction. Experience-lined lips slide into a wide smile like a five-year-old trying to catch a sea wave for the first time.

"Meet Shelby," My Boy says proudly. "She's a therapy dog."

"She is special," she whispers. "I feel it. She is gorgeous. I'm thrilled to make your acquaintance, Shelby. You have lifted a weight from my shoulders. I can't explain what happened, but I feel lighthearted, as if all the perplexing pieces of the puzzle will fit into place as they should."

"Careful, Mom," her daughter cautions, nervously anticipating with precision her mother's intention to lean over and pet me. I inch forward toward her. Our eyes lock. My heart flutters. I am living in the moment of God's will in action, and I am still in the parking area.

Before entering Hackensack University Medical Center to visit a special friend of Joe's, Jeff Rizzuto, almost three dozen people approach us. "Baby Girl, everyone is drawn to your magnetic, charismatic personality. Do you see how you pull everyone over to you?"

Who, me? Magnetic? Charismatic? I think Joe is biased because he loves me. I'm just Shelby the pit bull . . . and maybe on a good day, I'm cute.

"Let's go inside and see what happens," My Boy suggests. I hope we can get in. I want to be with Jeff. He's Phil Rizzuto's nephew and is very proud of his uncle's accomplishments as National Baseball Hall of Fame shortstop. Scooter, as he is nicknamed, played for the New York Yankees; Joe loves baseball.

Jeff, though still in the springtime of his life, on the cusp of forty, has been diagnosed with terminal cancer. I have been visiting him for several months, and he brightens when I enter the room and climb on his bed. His wife and children tell Joe they enjoy my company and the effect I have on him. Everyone just leaves behind the gravity of the situation for a few minutes.

This is my maiden visit as a therapy dog to a public facility. I know My Boy is concerned. I wonder why, though I recall overhearing him tell Geralynn during dinner last evening that he is a bit preoccupied about my entry to the facility. "It will be an unsurpassable milestone for her if she can do what she does best, love and minister to those in pain."

Yes, I trust God, but I confess to feeling a bit anxious. I hope my presence will not intimidate anyone. I will know shortly. Together, Joe and I walk through the large glass doors, our minds occupied in silent prayer, while God lends an ear from the heavens. Once inside the hospital, I accompany Joe to the reception desk. *God, this has to work*, I pray, *for My Boy and Jeff. I know this is part of your plan.*

"May I be of assistance?" the young receptionist inquires, smiling.

"I'm Joe Dwyer, and this is Shelby," he replies. "She's a certified therapy dog. We're here to see Jeff Rizzuto." Gently he slides my certification certificate across the counter. It never hurts to present "evidence"; it does, however, push rejection to a more heartbreaking level, should it occur.

Eyes lowered, she scans the papers and gazes at me with whimsey in her eyes. "Do you know Mr. Rizzuto's room number?" Choked with emotion, Joe lets out a raspy yes. My heartbeat accelerates. With her gracious permission to proceed, my therapy dog mission debuts. In a new prayer I hurriedly whisper: *My God, I need you more than ever as I embark on a different journey. Give me the patience to endure all in your name. Help me comfort and offer a few nurturing licks, especially to those who have debilitating battles ahead.*

"My child, I have given you the gift of a generous heart. Share your love with those locked in bitterness and despair. You have the power to rise above earthly ills and the power with your presence, to encourage

others to follow your path toward healing and forgiveness. Go now to Jeff—he begs for a reprieve from his agony. Go comfort him."

Everyone in the crowd sought to touch him because power came forth from him and healed them all.

~ Luke 6:19, NABRE

I keep praying during the elevator ride until we reach Jeff's floor. The sounds of bustling nurses and doctors scurrying about are not as intimidating as I initially thought. *Please, God, never leave my side*, I pray.

Jeff is not in his room. "Dialysis," I hear a technician tell Joe. Before entering to wait for his return, a middle-aged woman dressed in a hospital gown appears. "Can your dog come to visit me?" she asks, her gaze immobile in my direction.

"Sure," My Boy responds. "She is Shelby," he continues, beaming.

"Hello, Shelby," the woman responds, cradling my face between her hands. "It's a joy to have you here." My Boy's bald head is swelling with pride.

"Come," she invites, leading the way to her room. "Just meeting you has calmed my spirit and softened my pain." I turn to give Joe an affectionate look. He's ecstatic.

"You see, my child, this is another testament to your magnetism. People are drawn to your charm and charisma and to the gifts of understanding and compassion you share. Never fear approaching others, especially those who have misplaced their serenity."

God is truly with me. He knows I am a bit anxious about my maiden voyage as a therapy dog. Now I am feeling a bit stronger. Within minutes, Jeff's wife, Brenna, exits the elevator. Brenna's gaze falls directly on me. I wag my tail in greeting.

Petting my head, she blurts, "This is the famous Shelby that Jeff always mentions. He refers to her as his special angel. Now we will all see how right he is."

Blood rushes to my face. Honestly, I do not merit such praise. It does, however, fill My Boy with delight.

"Jeff should be here in a few," the nurse informs.

The sudden creak of the elevator door interrupts my thoughts. Turning, I see Jeff wheeled along the corridor on a gurney. My heart sinks. His face is drained of all color, his cheeks hollowed; he is a living portrayal of agony. I exchange glances with My Boy. He seems overwhelmed. I wait for the tug of my leash to enter Jeff's room.

"Shelby, you cannot jump on the bed because of the tubes and machines to which Jeff is attached," Joe cautions. Never at a loss for solutions, I apply my reserve plan. *Please, God, give strength to my legs*, I implore.

"Do not hesitate, my child. A suffering soul needs you. The sick should never be overlooked."

I glance over at Joe. His nod grants not only approval but encouragement. My Boy's endorsement, together with the strength from God, assures me I can do this. Without further hesitation I lift myself up, placing my front paws on the bed near Jeff's shoulders, positioning my face on the side of his chin. Responsive, he immediately inclines his head, establishing eye contact.

My heart races. I feel his breath on the tip of my nose. A moment of sadness ensues as I realize that one day, I will miss his breeze of life. Certainly, as an observer and participant, My Boy's pulse is thumping. He knows I am communicating to Jeff my love and admiration for his courageous battle. We have our own language. I encourage him to never abandon his will to go forward, regardless of the impending darkness. *I didn't, Jeff. I had faith and never gave up.*

They that hope in the Lord will renew their strength, they will soar on eagles' wings: They will run and not grow weary, walk and not grow faint.

~ Isaiah 40:31, NABRE

Jeff's ashen complexion, his brow furrowed in pain, his faint suggestion of a smile, almost unnatural, his leaden, lethargic demeanor—I seem to erase it all with a couple of wet, sticky kisses, just two licks of love. Even more striking is the pink coloring spreading along his quarried cheeks, together with the unwinding of deeply etched lines knotted across his forehead. When I see the glimmer of a genuine smile, I melt. *Did I do that, God?*

"Yes, my child—that is the power of love and nurturing."

Joe is overcome with emotion. I don't think he doubted, but in the face of eyewitness testimony, there is no disputing. "Jeff, we saw firsthand an incredible change," My Boy blurts, breathless.

"Joe, perhaps you don't realize the extent of Shelby's influence on me. She lifts me, body, mind, and spirit. It's as if I have swallowed a magic potion. Whenever she comes to the house, and in particular here in the hospital, I thrive in her presence: an angel, a very special angel. I think this rationalizes her immense suffering. God gave her the force to accept because He gave her the strength not only to endure and overcome but to understand the meaning of pain."

An almost hallowed stillness permeates the room. The episode is too emotional to vocalize—but not to catch a few tear drippings. "This is my Shelby, Jeff," Joe boasts. "A gift from God." Turning to me, he flashes a sweet, doting look. "Baby Girl, I'll take you home now. I think both you and Jeff need to rest."

I don't want to go home. There is much to do and many to help. Instead of moving toward the elevator, keeping pace with Joe, I reverse course, offering resistance. Tucked low between my legs, my tail hangs limp. Immediately, My Boy understands, redirects down the corridor, and we visit all the patients on Jeff's floor, leaving physicians and nurses speechless. Comforting the ailing is my reason to be, my life force.

In the late afternoon, we head home, tired but energized by the humble acceptance of God's mission for me. I feel a warm stirring in my heart for the blessing to see glowing eyes set in pained faces, many in anticipation of meeting their Creator.

Affirmation: "Love one another as I have loved you" requires patience, tolerance, a sacrifice of self-interests, and a generous heart.

CHAPTER XIV

Every tap of her paw, every wet nose nudging, every sweet, sticky
lick says, "I love you—I care—I'm here for you—you're not alone—I
understand your sadness." And Shelby knows full well the agony
of loneliness and abandonment as well as the excruciating pain of
physical abuse and humiliation.
~ *Shelby's Grace: From Abused Pup to Angel of Mercy,* Joe Dwyer

Joe and I spend many hours visiting the sick, men and women of all ages, in pain and often alone in their agony. I can relate by reflecting on the experiences from my first year of life. Since I faced my physical and mental turbulence unaccompanied by a compassionate soul, I do not want anyone to feel they walk their journey alone. In flashback, I cringe, reliving from time to time the sting of abandonment.

"My child, my gift of free will has allowed you to experience the dark side of life. Do you understand the merit reaped and the blessings received? When a hardship obstructed your path, you turned your attention to me while praying for the strength and ability to endure and overcome. Now, in return, you have a strong passion to assist those who suffer. Do you see the value in all that you experienced, my child? Do you see how you have grown. . . how you have become less about you and more about others?"

Therefore, I am content with weaknesses, insults, hardships,
persecutions, and constraints, for the sake of Christ; for when I am
weak, then I am strong.
~ 2 Corinthians 12:10, NABRE

I dare never contradict or doubt God. His all-knowing nature makes Him incapable of anything but the truth—He is the truth. My Boy has learned about life walking along his troubled paths. This is why we were designed to share our lives with each other and God's creatures. Our union is a team trailing in Christ's footsteps, administering to the suffering, the ostracized, and the lonely. It is why Joe and I leave every morning and head to the hospital.

But God has bigger plans to broaden my ministry, plans that include a new brother. Meanwhile, Joe has concluded a meeting at the Fort Worth, Texas, Pet Loss Professional Association Conference. After delivering a talk in preparation for the two-day workshop, he tunes in to the news while organizing his notes. Suddenly a newscaster breaks in. Pausing, My Boy focuses on the TV, learning an abandoned dog is being sent to New Jersey.

I know it's a quick trip because My Boy and I are scheduled for a presentation at a neighborhood school tomorrow, and Joe never defaults on a commitment. When I am asked to accompany him, my excitement level soars. I love kids of all ages and understand their, let's say, "growing pains."

"Joe just phoned, Shelby," Geralynn announces. "He'll be home tomorrow." *I wonder who is happier, me or Joe*, I muse. Perhaps it's a photo finish! "This evening he's running through his presentation one last time to be certain the delivery will be empowering and smooth. By the way, he asked if you miss him," she says playfully.

My Boy knows the answer, although Geralynn assures him that Sparty, Rommel, and Greta are keeping the house alive and animated and lifting my mood. What I don't know is that there are inklings of changes in the air. Excited about Joe's return, I can't sleep. I am, however, careful not to disturb my siblings.

After breakfast, Geralynn announces, "Joe will be here in about five minutes; he just texted." I move closer to the entry. When My Boy walks through the door, I try to contain myself to give Geralynn a few moments with him. But one look from him and I'm trying to reach his face for some welcome-home licks.

"Okay, Shelby," Joe laughs breathlessly. "I missed you too." *If you only knew how much*, I whisper. His loving glance tells me he knows. I melt. Following dinner, My Boy shows Geralynn the photo of a dog. As he speaks, his eyes darken. Something sad must have happened.

"This little dog was abandoned," he begins, "and faced euthanasia because his adoption was not finalized on a preestablished deadline." A tear escapes, sliding down his cheek. I catch it. Why wouldn't someone want him? "Sadly, no one came forward, and he was closed in the gas chamber with seventeen other pups to experience several agonizing minutes in anticipation of death." My stomach churns.

"My child, I know this is disturbing for you to hear, but it is one of life's realities. Thousands of unwanted dogs are gassed. It's a cruel and anguishing destiny. However, as you know, man has my gift of free will. Nevertheless, you and Joe will carry forth this crusade to save dogs' lives—it is part of your mission along with this beagle who I saved."

Much as I love my conversations with God, today I am completely befuddled and confess to having not even a minimal clue regarding His wishes for me. I pray I don't disappoint Him or Joe and that I will be able to carry out His plan.

Phone in hand, I hear my boy chatting about dogs—nothing surprising here. I listen. "It's too bad the adoption fell through. That cute beagle would make a nice fifth dog," My Boy says jokingly. Once intentions are set, they fly into the universe, be they serious or those amusingly spoken in jest.

Two days later, Joe receives a phone call from Jill, a foster mom for homeless pets. She announces she is stopping by with Daniel, the Miracle Beagle. My confusion multiples. No one can alter the course of God's plan.

When Geralynn joins us in the living room, My Boy tells a devastating story. "Geralynn, this little dog survived the gas chamber. Every other dog died an atrocious death. It is shameful, inhumane treatment, a deplorable commentary on the mistreatment of God's creatures, and difficult to accept as a twenty-first-century reality. All living, breathing participants in creation have a right to live the life their Creator intended. There is a message here for me."

My Boy knows he was summoned to make a difference—to change the tide of transgressive practices and give honor and dignity to every heart that beats. God's words are still unclear, though the clouds of confusion are opening up. I have to be patient and trusting.

The anticipated day arrives. 11th Hour Rescue, and PetResQ, two amazing organizations, are responsible for Daniel the Miracle Beagle's trip to New Jersey and the visit. Joe seems to have something in mind.

At the first meeting, my brother Sparty is guarded and not a very welcoming host. There seems to be an issue of conflicting personalities, which is not surprising, considering Sparty's alpha male status in the house. Meanwhile, Greta and Rommel approach their guest, sniffing and seemingly gracious, wagging their tails in greeting. Having overcome the hesitancy of youth, Daniel makes a run to my side. Perhaps viewing death face-to-face has matured his life perspective, giving him a just-grab-the-moment-before-it's-gone mindset. There is instant chemistry. Daniel and I click immediately. Yes, I do believe in love at first sight: first with My Boy, and now with the Miracle Beagle.

Joe is pleased, though Sparty's unsurprising demeanor concerns him. My Boy is an emissary of peace; thus, his home attracts love without boundaries. Here before him is an obstacle—a doxie and a beagle.

God, I like Daniel. Can you help us here? You did save Daniel from the lions! And the beagle has his name. He also has done no wrong!

My God sent his angel and closed the lions' mouths so that they have not hurt me. For I have been found innocent before him; neither have I done you any harm, O king!

~ Daniel 6:23

"My child, do not worry needlessly. Remember my words to you clearly: this beagle will be saved. Have faith, and trust me. He was saved for a purpose. All my creatures are born with peace in their hearts. Sometimes, life choices cloud the eyes, build obstacles. You and Joe are here to remove complications and restore peace. Trust me—it is all I ask."

I trust and I pray. By the third visit, Sparty seems to have worked through his issues and accepts Daniel. I am thrilled to have a new brother. But what if My Boy loves him more than me?

"My child, do not indulge in foolish thinking. Joe has a great capacity to love my four-pawed children. You know you are his heartbeat, his special angel. No one will ever come between you. Now have faith and do not waver. Your mission is about to expand."

Although I am sorry to upset God, I am grateful for His reprimand. It straightens me and lifts a weight from my shoulders. Here is a dog in need of love and nurturing, a survivor of brutality. We have that in common. But there is a "to be continued" . . . many filaments are being intertwined for a new purpose.

In the meantime, Daniel's fame as a survivor suddenly brings an outpouring of offers for adoption, with one individual actually offering six figures for him. Joe talks about the misfortune of opportunism. "This is not what it is meant to be."

Thankfully, everything works out and I gain a little brother. We chat for hours while everyone is asleep, exchanging life stories and sharing wisdom learned along the way. Daniel confides his horrifying tale of the seventeen dogs crying and cringing in pain as the poisonous gas attacked their organs and obstructed their breathing.

Shelby, it was awful—an excruciating twenty minutes of hell. I was powerless and could not help. One by one they died, choking and gagging, cruelly suffocated. I prayed for salvation and gave my word I would always behave if granted a miracle. Now I don't know what is expected of me—but I want to give back for my eleventh-hour reprieve.

Shelby, I have to tell you about Pilots 'n Paws. They flew me here. Usually, they transport abandoned dogs to different localities to be adopted and handle all the financial responsibilities. The word is that they operate through donations. Such nice guys.

And when those hired about the eleventh hour came, each of them received a denarius.
~ Matthew 20:9, ESV

Daniel, that is quite a frightful story. God did not intend torture for His creatures. But as He always says, He gave humans the gift of free will. This is why you, me, and Joe were brought together. We have a mission to assist troubled men, women, and children, and halt the slaughter of innocent animals by highlighting your story.

Once comfortable on the soft cushion Geralynn bought me, I can't stop the tears for the initial fate of my little brother. I pray no one will hurt another fragile, vulnerable animal. God listens to my prayers; too bad the special gift of free will sometimes goes awry.

My brother is rambunctious, playful, and as Joe affectionally says, a clown, but so full of love and energy to just get up and go nonstop. Notoriety never tampers with his sunny personality. Suddenly most of the news channels in New York and New Jersey broadcast Daniel's story. I am seated beside Joe when suddenly the newscaster announces: *"A beagle is dragged into the gas chamber to die—and he doesn't. He just doesn't die!"*

Soon after, Daniel becomes quite a celebrity, but Joe is careful never to exhaust him. "I want him to enjoy being a dog" is My Boy's banner phrase. "Shelby also. Yes, I hope that you, Daniel, and I can be spokespeople against all forms of brutality targeting humans and animals: the gas chamber, bullying and prejudice, loneliness and abandonment, but not at your expense. Your well-being is my priority."

Soon we become busy. Joe sits quietly scribbling notes, appointment dates, and addresses on scraps of paper. First, there is the protest rally at the Thorncroft Equestrian Center in Philadelphia to share Daniel's story and fight for the repeal of the gas chamber for unwanted dogs. The goal is to repeal the law throughout the United States. I am so proud when Senator Andrew Dinniman, charmed by Daniel's gracious charisma, introduces Daniel's Law (Senate Bill 1329) to end the use of gas chambers in Pennsylvania and confers on the Miracle Beagle the title of poster dog for the law.

Next, Daniel is invited by Anderson Cooper, an animal rights advocate, to be interviewed on his show. I am more nervous than my little brother, but he, Joe, and Geralynn are a big hit, and God's message about the sanctity of all life is broadcast nationally.

There is also the Hero Dog Award honor for exceptional, courageous, and heroic pups, sponsored and transmitted on the Hallmark Channel. Joe and Daniel present themselves in black ties.

"Geralynn, it is an amazing event and commentary on the importance of dogs in our lives." My Boy looks so handsome in his tuxedo. I am so proud. He even enjoys a nice conversation with the lovely animal rights advocate Betty White, who adores animals.

Despite all the fun celebrity events, my best time is visiting schools together with Daniel and Joe. All three of us have challenging stories that have taught us priceless lessons. Now it is time to impress upon children that a positive attitude, self-esteem, and faith in themselves conquer the demons. Whereas just quitting is the open door to failure and unhappiness.

Joe speaks about treating each other with respect. "Never ridicule anyone, whether or not there are differences, because all humans are born equal, and everyone may be going through a difficult moment," he says. Of course, Joe and I share a strong feeling for bullying, having walked that path personally, me because I am a pit bull, and Joe because of his skin issues. My Boy repeats continually, "Prejudice and the mistreatment of others are based on ignorance; therefore, our mission is to try to defeat this deprivation early on."

Days are full, gratifying, and overabounding with joy, between the hospital visits and the school talks. The children love me and Daniel, and relate to the lessons Joe imparts after hearing our stories. My Boy is a genius—he has discovered a wonderful way to relax children, and not only grab their attention but hold it.

"Shelby, Daniel, you have just a minute or two to make a connection—if you do, you will have your audience; if you don't, you won't."

I notice that Joe is very busy between our school and hospital visits. He sits for hours at his desk working on the computer. In a little while, I will try to discover what is going on. I see him standing and stretching. This is my cue to interrupt.

"My child, Joe is busy and focused on authoring a book. This is a very special project, and he needs some quiet time to gather his thoughts. Pray for him."

I'm so curious and want to know everything about Joe. Geralynn is going to his office. I trail behind. "What are you doing, Joe? You look so intense. You seem to be spending a lot of time at your computer. Is it a secret project?" She laughs playfully.

"No, I am writing a book about Shelby—her life and her amazing mission. The title will be *Shelby's Grace: From Abused Pup to Angel of Mercy!*"

Forcing my tail into motionless mode while withdrawing my breath, I inch away from the door, tears streaming down my face, my heart racing. *A book, God? A book about me?* My Boy is a writer—an author? I wonder what it is about. *God, please help me find out.*

"Yes, my child, Joe is writing your life story for all to read, for all to be inspired, and for all to love you, as is my intention."

Affirmation: Only God can create loving relationships held firm in a special, everlasting bond.

CHAPTER XV

There is an appointed time for everything, and a time for every affair under the heavens. A time to give birth, and a time to die; a time to plant, and a time to uproot the plant.
~ Ecclesiastes 3:1–2, NABRE

And there is a time to say goodbye, for God created the world and *invited* all His living creations to live in harmony. Sadly, life doesn't always unravel according to plan, but once the gift of freedom is given, it is never withdrawn. However, He navigates the heartbeats of humans and animals, as the Divine Creator.

"My child, you may not always understand my ways, but you must trust in my actions, even if painful. Have faith in my will, and I will always give you the strength to endure and overcome. Remember, tears began when Adam and Eve defied my wishes. In life there is accountability. You know I created the animals before humans. They never caused me sorrow; they never defied me."

"And to all the beasts of the earth and all the birds in the sky and all the creatures that move along the ground—everything that has the breath of life in it—I give every green plant for food." And it was so.
~ Genesis 1:30, NIV

Once again, I do not fully understand God's words, but fear hides, entwined in this confusion. I am not calm. I will go to My Boy to make certain he is not encountering any hardship.

"Hi, Baby Girl," Joe calls, as if listening to my thoughts. He seems fine, though I sense an aura of sadness. "Let's sit here a moment. I want to talk to you."

Time with My Boy is always special. To show my appreciation, I make my way over to where he is sitting and rest my head on his thigh, but not before giving one long, sweeping lick from his chin to his forehead. He tastes different, perhaps because he just shaved.

"Shelby, I want to prepare you for the inevitable. You know that everyone is born with a special purpose and their life falls into place accordingly. God's plan is beautiful, but it involves disappointments—disappointments like sickness and death."

Joe is scaring me, God. Please don't let My Boy get sick or die. Is he sick? I would not be able to live without him.

"My child, Joe is fine, but you will soon receive some disturbing news. Be strong and remain close to Joe. He will need you."

God has me worried, even if reassured that My Boy enjoys good health. The mystery is being unraveled, the untold spoken. "Shelby, your brother Sparty is very elderly and seriously ill. Soon I fear he will leave us. Heartbreaking as it is, we must be accepting of the cycles of life."

Joe's words are dire and hint at an immoveable finality. And so, it occurs as the divine designed it. Sparty crosses over, leaving us fighting an intense sorrow. The little doxie, affectionately referred to as the Boss, was My Boy's first rescue.

Daniel looks at me somberly. I don't think he fully understands the finality of death. Joe, Geralynn, and Jenna are in tears. I wish I could help, but my heart feels just as heavy as theirs. I will miss my brother Sparty.

Shelby, everyone seems overwhelmed with sadness, Daniel whispers. *He will wake up soon, won't he?*

No, Daniel. Sparty has died. He will never return. Death is not reversible. God gives life, but then life ends for all living things. Don't you remember the tall red flowers Joe bought for Geralynn? We stood and watched as they opened wide to their full beauty. And then they closed up, hung their heads, and died. This is the meaning of life—the story of creation.

But Shelby, it is heart-wrenching. Joe is in such pain.

Daniel, we can lick his tears, remain close, and give him a little extra love, I whisper. *We all lost love today, a special love, Sparty's love. Death and loss are painful, but not for Sparty—he is with God. The suffering is ours to bear.*

We will never play with him again, the Miracle Beagle whimpers.

In heaven we will, Daniel. In heaven where God lives.

"My child, Daniel is young, but I depend on you to give him the wisdom of life you have acquired along your journey of trials. Life is about learning and sharing knowledge with others. Life is about living, empowered by the breath of life I gave to humans and animals."

Soon after, with the flight of months and years, Rommel and Greta are summoned to their final destinies. The goodbyes never get easier; to the contrary, they hurt so deeply. The unconditional love lost is unbearable to endure. Purity, like the soul of an animal, overwhelms with joy. When it is taken, it is devastating.

"Shelby, although our little doxies have departed, they remain in our hearts and thoughts," Joe says, his voice cracking. Each presence is honored with a photo and memento in My Boy's office; each absence is a unique memory. How sweet and welcoming they were to me upon my arrival. Such a treasure lost.

Daniel and I keep the spirits elevated in the house with our personalities, mine warm and nurturing, his crazy, distracting, and stress-releasing. My

Miracle Beagle brother is an anecdote of energy, and although I am feeling some of the consequences of the years, I keep pace. Joe is never left to himself, even if he should wish for an interlude of tranquility. Many times, My Boy and Daniel make overnight trips. Though I miss them, I know they are fulfilling their God-given purpose to ensure every dog is granted the life they were born to live and a loving family and home to love. My boy is committed to animal advocacy. He has started a rescue, named Daniel's Dream, in honor of my brother.

"My child, you have grown in the knowledge of wisdom. Yours is a life well experienced. You understand that Joe is following the pathway I designed with both you and Daniel. Nevertheless, I advised him to let you be dogs also. This is my plan for animals. Joe will make certain it is honored."

Then God said: Let the earth bring forth every kind of living creature:
tame animals, crawling things, and every kind of wild animal.
And so it happened . . .
God saw that it was good.
~ Genesis 1:24–25, NABRE

My Boy seems to have brightened up a bit. Every few weeks he meets with the sweet woman who cut the irritating shackles fastening me to the fence outside the gas station. Quietly I recline at an appropriate distance, not to disturb, yet close enough to eavesdrop on the conversation. I hear Joe lament about the plight of suffering, abandoned dogs. His demeanor of dejected melancholy screams for some licks. It's frustrating. *Please, God, give me the strength to resist.*

Listening, I detect a sudden indescribable tone of bliss in his voice at the mention of my name. He appears air-lifted and carefree—even if just for a fleeting moment. Tail wagging, warm dog breath and moist, sticky licks have that effect on My Boy—a miraculous, transformational effect. But nothing in life is enduring, not even the most stunning sunrise painted by the divine hand against the backdrop of an unmarred azure sky.

Today is a cool autumn October Sunday, great for playing outdoors with Daniel. Prayers completed, Geralynn serves breakfast. Though not a hearty eater, I always clean my plate, careful never to leave behind even a tiny scrap. Joe says it is sinful to waste food when a multitude of dogs are facing the day hungry. As usual, I continue eating while Daniel, his dining manners more in tune with gulping than savoring, impatiently dances around, already in digestion. After breakfast, before going out I give Geralynn a big lick. I have to be careful because sometimes she wears makeup, so I don't want to ruin her artistic work. On the other hand, with My Boy, it's a no-boundary licking territory from his chin up to and including his bald head.

Both Joe and Geralynn receive their morning gratitude licks, and it's off to the yard. Once in the breezy air, Daniel is up for some playtime. Suddenly a strong stabbing pain in my stomach snatches my breath away. Taken by surprise, I let out a screech. The uncommon behavior brings Joe running.

"Is everything all right, Shelby? Did you see something that scared you?" I nuzzle his hand in reassurance, unwilling to cause him concern. My stomach hurts badly. When we enter the house, I position myself next to Joe. The screech escapes before I can control or smother it. *God, what is happening? Why am I in so much pain?*

"My child, take to heart my words: There is 'a time to weep, and a time to laugh; a time to mourn, and a time to dance' [Ecclesiastes 3:4, NABRE]. I will remain close to you always."

I am unable to hide my discomfort. Joe knows me too well and is ultrasensitive to my needs. Sliding closer, he cradles my head in his hands. "Something is not right with you, Baby Girl. Tomorrow we will visit the vet—just for the reassurance that all is well." But, is it?

A trained professional eye notices more than someone who is always around, therefore when the vet remarks that I have lost 10% of my body weight, My Boy seems both surprised and scared. Something in the pit of my stomach jumps. A fierce bout of nausea runs through me. Something is very wrong; a specialist is advised. The pain throbs.

During the examination, a noticeable bump on my leg becomes a point of great concern for the internist. I gaze at My Boy just in time to catch his lower lip quiver ever so slightly. *God, what is happening? You said a time to weep.*

"My child, you must be strong for Joe."

I don't understand God's message. It triggers inklings of sadness. Of course, I will oblige His wishes. When Joe calls, I go to him. "Baby Girl, we have to return to the vet," he informs. "I'm sorry, but I want the pains to end." My tail wags to signal all is well, though it isn't. I do not believe my little white lie is harmful. *God, you did say be strong for Joe. I am trying. It is I who need your help.*

Once again, the vet presses and twists my sore leg. The pain is agonizing. Slowly I turn my head away from Joe. I don't want him to see my grimace. He will suffer more knowing I am in agony.

"Joe, I don't see anything serious," the doctor informs, "but to be certain I would advise a scope. Meanwhile, I will treat Shelby with prednisone." My Boy smiles, relieved; I cringe inside. Hope can be a double-edged sword where false and true sit at opposing ends. Only one will take precedence. More inklings of sadness. Something is not right.

Although the scope is inconclusive, the vet surmises gastritis but speaks openly, detailing the situation. "Joe, unfortunately, I cannot rule out a malignancy. However, to pinpoint specifically, I would have to invasively go into the lining of her stomach. It is risky."

"I would prefer not to put her through such a radical and risky procedure at this time," My Boy responds. I exhale, somewhat relieved. A sense of impending darkness continues. I feel restlessness within, an anxiety, hard to overcome.

"Give her the medication, Joe, and let's see how she does." My appetite improves and I finish my dinner, leaving not even a trace behind. Thankfully I have never been a speed eater like Daniel, so my leisurely pace is of no immediate concern. Joe watches, attuned with every move I make. I don't want to worry him.

Veering toward the winter solstice, the days gradually darken earlier, and the morning breezes are cooler. Sometimes I shudder, though Daniel's energy engaging me in play seems to warm the air. He is such a delightful playmate. I wish I have the energy of my early years to keep up with him.

Don't worry, Shelby. I can play more gently too—for you. He's nutty and effervescent, my little brother, but I love him dearly. A terrible experience took his puppyhood innocence, and I always feel a softness in my heart for him, as I do for all who suffer. Of course, the first place in my heart is reserved for Joe—no one can ever occupy that place of honor.

My stomach hurts this evening, with a throbbing incessant rhythm, and I have the urge to move my bowels. It is cold now, uncomfortable to be outdoors in the raw night air. Every couple of minutes, I have to bother My Boy to take me out. I see the fearful look crossing his face. I know he is praying. I am praying also. My heart grows heavy.

"Baby Girl, come over here," he invites, pointing to the sofa. "I will sleep beside you and we can go outside whenever you need to." I am crying silently, in the refuge of my mind. Joe must not know. I place my paw over his hand to let him understand I love him and want to comfort him. *Who, God? Who will when . . ."*

Finally, My Boy dozes off: Anxiety is exhausting.

"My child, the cycle of life continues, pausing for no one. You have fulfilled your purpose to perfection. Your relationship with Joe is inspiring. Only I know the strength and capacity of your love. Joe will go forth as I am directing and teach others the beauty, joy, and miraculous gifts exchanged when animals and humans bond, sharing reciprocal love and respect. Let Joe care for you now as you cared for him. The cycle of life is coming full swing. It is my way."

I know I am declining, even if the new medication does offer me an improved quality of life. The holidays, however, bring uplifted spirits. I am trying my best to contradict the inevitable. I have cancer. It's real now—the fear I always feared. It's no longer unmotivated. My leg is agonizing, swollen, red, and burns, extremely painful to the touch. Joe schedules another visit with the vet. I like her: she's professionally savvy and so compassionate with a delicate touch when palpating my stomach. She really cares.

The news is dire. I wish I could change God's mind, but He feels I have accomplished much, helped many, and, together with Joe, paved the way for all animals to enjoy a dignified existence.

"My child, be prepared to come home. Don't worry about Joe. You will always be with him, just as you were during his growing-up years. It is time."

Amen, amen, I say to you, the hour is coming and is now here when the dead will hear the voice of the Son of God, and those who hear will live.

~ John 5:25

"Baby Girl, let's sit here a moment," Joe says. "I hope you understand how much I love you." A tear slips down his cheek. My heart is in shambles. My intuition tells me this is the beginning of goodbye. *I don't want to go, Joe, I don't want to leave you*, I whimper. *Do you hear me? God wishes for you to continue defending animals. I know you will never disappoint Him. That's who you are, My beloved Boy.*

"Thank you, Shelby—thank you for my life. You saved it; now it's yours. God sent you to empower and inspire, teach and comfort, just as you did. I love you, Shelby; you will always be a part of me. Not solely because I want, but because God designed us embracing each other. Baby Girl, He crossed our paths for a lifetime."

The following morning a sweet young woman arrives. Cancer has weakened my body and I am unable to stand. Joe places me on my big, soft pillow and gently caresses my head. Geralynn leans over and kisses me. *I love you*, I whimper, *thank you*. I do not want them to cry. I try to be brief. Daniel sweeps by and licks my face several times. *Daniel, please keep an eye on Joe for me. He will be devastated. I love you, Daniel. Thanks for all the fun times.* When Joe leans over to kiss me, my insides explode—such pain is indescribable. I say nothing. My Boy prefers it this way. He knows what is in my heart. His tears tell all. It is his wish that I don't see . . . but Joe knows he cannot hide anything from me. In a year he will have a beautiful surprise. God has given me His word.

The injection is a slight pinch, and with my last breath a mere echo in time, I return to where it all began, beside my Creator, now with memories instead of longings. *Thank you, God, for Joe, and thank you for a beautiful life. Thank you!*

Affirmation: True love, inspired by God, never, ever ends.

CHAPTER XVI

Until one has loved an animal, a part of one's soul remains
unawakened.
~ Anatole France

Much as I miss playing with Daniel and feeling his captivating energy reinvigorate me after a tiring day at the hospital, I have to admit it is an absolute delight to follow his paths, guided of course by Joe. His miracle certainly did not end with his walk of survival the moment he exited the gas chamber. My brother's miracle was wrapped in a very special package—the mission.

"This is true, my child. I granted Daniel the miracle of his life, a second chance. He was saved to save others. It makes me happy to see the work he and Joe are doing to bring awareness to the gas chamber option for abused and abandoned dogs and cats and to promote adoptions. Frisky, fun-loving, and a bit of a clown, as Joe likes to tease, he has power in his paws and generous licks."

Before I formed you in the womb I knew you, before you were born, I
set you apart; I appointed you as a prophet to the nations.
~ Jeremiah 1:5, NIV

I love when God speaks about my little brother. It warms my heart to know my Creator feels Daniel is fulfilling his purpose and following in the divine plan designed for him. I have been *with* my boy since his childhood and so continue to be. Likewise, I will continue to walk beside Daniel. My love never ends, nor will it ever, despite the fact I am in another realm.

I see Joe is involved in preparing the morning meal for Daniel and Bella. Meticulous, each has his/her special bowl and correct portion size. Bella seems to have a rather hearty appetite. Why not? She is a big, tall, muscular young girl. With the manners of a gentleman, compliments of My Boy's mentoring, Daniel pauses, allowing his sister to safely complete her mad dash to the breakfast bowls. I think he has something to say to her—I know that look on his face when he wishes to *speak.*

Bella, Daniel begins, *Joe and I are visiting a school this morning. We used to go with Shelby, my big sister who is now with God. Many times I am sad because you didn't get to know her. She was an angel—altruistic, kind, compassionate, and always concerned with the welfare of others. She lived to make life sweeter for those crossing difficult times. Like the legend of Androcles who pulled the thorn from the paw of the lion and in gratitude befriended the kind man bringing him life-saving nourishment, Shelby pulled thorns from many "feet" alleviating discomfort, demonstrating her empathy and thankfulness. I only hope I can give Joe half of all that she did and neither fall short nor disappoint.*

Tears cloud my vision, but within seconds I see Bella lovingly listen to her big brother's words, her eyes fixed on his wagging tail; thoughts of me always excite him. She seems rather reserved, so unlike Daniel, but I know she has a heart full of love. As God taught me, everything has a time—His time. Therefore, patience I must continue to conquer.

Joe and Daniel climb into the car. Probably they are heading to a middle school where My Boy will open a discussion about the devastation and harmful effects of toxic bullying. He will also introduce the concept of prejudice and bias, using me, often misjudged for being a pit bull, as an example. Children and teens must understand the failings of ignorance-based discrimination. By his side will stand my brother, until after the talk. Eventually, he will roam the room greeting the kids with his signature kisses. The adolescents love him and look forward to his interventions. Today he seems exceedingly energetic; maybe I detect a slight impatience. I think he needs a bit of big sister advice.

Daniel. I catch his attention. Immediately he recognizes my wish to communicate and stands still. *Be calm with rough or clumsy petting. It is not purposeful. Kids are kids and don't realize they may be heavy-handed in demonstrating their love and affection. They are all going through something, just as I did and you did. Be sweet.*

I mastered that early on. It was, however, very challenging in the beginning. Every raised and extended hand in my visual field led to a tightening in my stomach. I shut my eyes, feeling the pain of the beatings I received as a young pup. Joe healed my PTSD moments. He healed with the most powerful and efficient medication, a medication with absolutely no adverse side effects. He healed with a very special brand of Joe's love therapy.

Daniel hears my message: *I miss you so much, Shelby, and long to see you again. Will it ever happen? Will we play together? Will we walk beside Joe while he speaks to us, sharing his wisdom, telling us where we are going while he prepares us for the school visit and our encounter with the kids? Do you remember, Shelby, what a great connection we had in those classrooms? The children relaxed, forgetting for a moment their difficult family situations and personal adolescent challenges. I will continue in your paw-steps, Shelby. But why did you leave us?*

My heart is breaking. Much as I feel his sadness, there are certain circumstances of life he cannot understand—not while he is on earth. And I also must be accepting of my physical absence in their lives.

Joe and Daniel hold firm in their crusade against gas-chamber euthanasia, which still occurs. His words to Geralynn ring endearingly: "If we can ban this barbarous practice in Ohio, it would be a great accomplishment."

"You and Daniel will do it," she responds, smiling. "One by one it will happen."

"We played our part, together with some equally committed animal rescue organizations, and were successful in more than twenty states so far. Now I'm taking Daniel to the vet for his physical and rabies shot. He's probably not happy about it, but it's a necessary inconvenience to avoid a serious issue."

I am laughing as Daniel runs into the kitchen. He knows better. Extremely cautious about the well-being of all his children, human and animal, Joe will persist. Like it or not, my brother will be visited and vaccinated, just as I was. In the end, it's just a slight pinch, an inconvenience for the greater good.

The vet is waiting, happy to see Joe and Daniel. I doubt the feeling is mutual on my brother's part.

"Joe, I see that Daniel has lost several pounds. Is he eating properly?" My Boy seems surprised.

"Yes, he eats with gusto. There is no need to ever scrape his bowl. And he is as active as ever. Now that Bella has joined the family and during this COVID pandemic, we cover more territory on our walks. Perhaps that explains his drop in weight."

"Just give him more food and let's see how he handles it. I will wait on the rabies shot. Bring him back in two weeks and we'll monitor how he does with added calories."

I listen, somewhat puzzled.

I sought the LORD, and he answered me, delivered me from all my fears.

~ Psalm 34:5

"My child, you are pensive today. My plan is designed, and in time it will come to fruition. Be accepting."

My trust in God is unwavering, unlike on earth where occasionally I slipped and questioned some of His actions, especially during moments in which My Boy was overtaken with sadness. Nevertheless, inklings of change interrupt my thoughts at different intervals: inexplicable feelings in arrival and departure, like dawn and dusk. Nothing in life is ever certain, not even our heartbeats. What is God's plan?

Today after two weeks, Joe and Daniel return to the vet. The extra meal rations have resulted in a several-pound weight gain. The vet is pleased, and My Boy is delirious with joy when told his buddy recuperated the loss. Life is back on track.

The heat begins to escalate. It's the 17th of June, and I'm happy Joe seems immersed in the outline of his next motivational talk. Driven to inspire, encourage, and defend the vulnerable, his passion is to better the lives of all living creatures. I notice Daniel seems happy, playing with Bella. Joe seizes the moment to take a breather. Closing his eyes, perhaps hoping for a brief nap, he dozes off. It's a beautiful scene from up here. I wish I could join them physically, not just as a spectator.

Suddenly my brother seems disturbed. Why? All is calm and everyone is resting. I see him leave Joe's office. A rustle outdoors instigates a bark reaction from Bella. My Boy bolts to his feet. But where is Daniel? Puzzled, Joe walks to Daniel's bedroom. His beloved beagle is stretched out on the bed. When their eyes link, his tail wags an all-is-well greeting. My Boy smiles and returns to his office.

However, at dinner time, when Bella and Daniel are summoned, he does not heed the call. An ominous cloud bypasses the horizon. Another inkling invades my calm. Joe and Geralynn are perplexed.

"You can let Bella eat, Geralynn. I will look for Daniel. His behavior is strange."

Searching for my brother, Joe notices various areas of the house with easily recognizable carpet stains. My brother is vomiting. Something is askance, and I am concerned. Several hours later he refuses all nourishment. "If he is not better in the morning, I will take him to the vet." Geralynn nods her approval, and a worried look crosses her face. I pray there will not be a rush to melancholic thoughts. I feel helpless. Joe and Daniel need me.

"My child, all things drift to a conclusion. This is the core of life. My creatures must be accepting, be it in serenity or confusion. You are with them in thought. Fear not, for I will take care of each one as soon as the hour strikes."

Have I not commanded you? Be strong and courageous. Do not be afraid; do not be discouraged, for the LORD your God will be with you wherever you go.

~ Joshua 1:9, NIV

I see Daniel take a few licks of water. It doesn't stay with him. My Boy remains vigilant, comforting him throughout the night, his arms wrapped around him for support as he did many nights with me, Sparty, Greta, and Rommel. This is who he is—this is the depth of his love for us. I see he is praying. I join him.

The situation seems to precipitate. In the morning Joe takes my brother to the vet for some testing. The doctor's words are upsetting. "Joe, I'm worried. Daniel has lost weight again and his blood count is low. He is anemic. I'd like him to have an ultrasound, but I'm afraid there's a two-week wait." I prepare for some gunfire blasts!

"Two weeks!" My Boy shouts. "He is losing weight and can't keep any nourishment down. I need a diagnosis now and a treatment. I will not allow him to suffer for a couple of weeks in this unknown agony."

Leaving the office visibly irritated by his inability to get help, My Boy calls a friend from the car, a rescue friend who has a good relationship with another vet.

"Joe, call me back in five minutes," Donna Rasulo from the Rescue Haven Foundation blurts. The longest five minutes imaginable. "Okay, you have an appointment right now, so get driving!" *Thank you, God. Thy will be done, but please don't let my little brother suffer, and please take Joe's hand.*

X-rays and ultrasound completed, Dr. Anthony Scriffignano from the Verona Animal Hospital approaches Joe. My Boy's eyes survey his in silent supplication—searching, desperately searching for a faint flicker of hope. Instead, darkness prevails. Chills run their course along my spine.

"I'm sorry, Joe. I have bad news. The ultrasound revealed a large mass under Daniel's rib cage and various growths on other organs. His lungs are full of tumors. I'm afraid it may be hemangiosarcoma, a highly aggressive blood-vessel cancer." Joe's eyes are welling up.

Daniel's fate is inarguably ominous. I see devastation steal a path through My Boy. I'm heartbroken. Nothing and no one will be a comfort to Joe. My tendency to run to him, to comfort him, to love him, and to cover his face with licks remains inoperative. My inclination to be with my brother likewise falls dormant. *Please, God, please help them. Please lighten some of the suffering and pain.*

"My child, it is Daniel's time, just as it was your time and just as it was my time on the Cross. Joe will not let him suffer, just as you didn't either, difficult as it is to say goodbye."

Therefore, just as through one person, sin entered the world, and through sin, death, and thus death came to all, inasmuch as all sinned.
~ Romans 5:12, NABRE

Both the diagnosis and prognosis are fatalistic. Although scientifically, absolute certainty cannot be assured, the consensus speculates that the cancer-causing agent may have been the toxic fumes my brother inhaled in the gas chamber. Unwilling to surrender to the inevitable, My Boy consults several noted oncologists: chemo and radiation will leave Daniel dreadfully sick and miserable in exchange for a couple of months of poor-quality life. Is it fair to await death, treading along a route of anguishing thorns? Is it fair to preserve the breath of a dying creature of God for selfish reasons?

Decision made, My Boy tries the holistic approach, phoning a highly recommended vet in Deerfield Beach, Florida. "It's too late, Joe. From the medical reports you read me, there is no hope. I cannot offer any healing. I'm so sorry."

Joe appreciates the vet's honesty. Experience has taught me he would spend down to his last cent for Daniel, for all of us. He will debate with his Creator until the bitter end. Seeking another pathway, he consults another holistic vet who writes a script for some pain medication and natural remedies to assure my brother more comfort. Sometimes it seems as if our merciful God has selected noble souls to redeem vulnerable individuals. Did not the Son of God suffer atrocious agonies to save even the worst of His creatures? And so, Daniel suffered appallingly in the gas chamber for the salvation of other animals. His thinking, fully shared and supported by Joe, involved a mission to increase adoptions—this in itself would eliminate the need for gas-chamber euthanasia.

Daniel has fought a hero's battle, surprising no one. To the victor belong the spoils—triumphant, he started his days fighting for his life in the gas chamber and ended with the same never-relinquishing spirit. However, this time, God has called, and Daniel obeys. In Joe's arms, their eyes meet. *I love you so much, Joe. Thank you for all the love and for defending all animals. Remember we talked about Ohio. I know you will keep the cause alive. I hope you know how much I love you, and Geralynn too. Thank you. His tongue comes forward for the last time, swiping my boy's finger.*

When Joe kisses his Miracle Beagle, his best buddy goodbye, my heart flutters. Though he is unaware how blissful is the calming effect of Dr. Scriffignano's injection to eternity, Daniel's face is soaked with Joe's tears, soaked like the head of a newborn, just baptized. And thus my brother crosses the Rainbow Bridge. Excited, I prepare with indescribable happiness to greet my little brother, ironically tinged with intense despondency.

Just moments thereafter, as the Miracle Beagle undertakes his journey home to his Creator, the news breaks—a bill is signed in Ohio to ban euthanasia via the gas chamber: June 29, 2021.

The victory is bittersweet. My Boy sobs, devastated, inconsolable, clutching Daniel's lifeless body in his arms. I want so badly to run to him. My tears mix with his. *God, I thought there were no tears in heaven!*

"My child, there is unconditional happiness in my heaven; there are tears only when an animal comes home to me, so painful is the loss on earth."

No paradise will heaven ever be unless I recognize and feast my eyes upon my beloved dogs.
~ Joe Dwyer, remembering Fritz, Sparty, Greta, Rommel, Shelby, Daniel . . . and the many forthcoming

Affirmation: A hero's priority is to help others, and even when they pass away, their memory lives to inspire others to aid those in need.

AFTERWORD

An animal's eyes have the power to speak a great language.
~ Martin Buber

Life teaches us. Schools and learning institutes offer book knowledge, running us through, as many will agree, rather strenuous brain gymnastics for cerebral development and the ability to think as logical, rational people with sufficient data and skills to make educated, profitable decisions. Interactions with family, friends, clergy and spiritualists, colleagues, and various individuals, professional and otherwise, raise the curtain on the vicissitudes of the human condition. But is all this enough? Does it equip us to live harmonious, well-balanced, happy, serene lives? Don't expect an answer. Why? Simply because the answer is yours to supply.

During my motivational talks and encounters with various people, I sometimes pose the question: "Do you think all these wonderful accomplishments and offerings provide an integrated life education?" The responses from people of all walks of life are identical. "Sure, Joe. What else is there? Get a good education and get a good job." Of course, I am a proponent of the acquisition of knowledge, having earned a degree. Was it the key to a perfect life? Absolutely not!

Sadly, too many individuals seeking enlightenment and the means to resolve some of life's challenges often fail to realize that the best instructors have never earned fancy university degrees. They do, however, possess the prerequisites necessary for winning the jewel of enlightenment—wisdom. "Prerequisites, Joe?" "Yes, four paws and a tail!"

In the words of Marc Bekoff, PhD, professor emeritus of ecology and evolutionary biology at the University of Colorado: "Let us remember that animals are not mere resources for human consumption. They are splendid beings in their own right, who have evolved alongside us as co-inheritors of all the beauty and abundance of life on this planet."

I have gathered sufficient experience to judge what exactly has been and continues to be my greatest source of wisdom. Undoubtedly, it has been my relationship with my seven dogs. As diverse as the world's ethnic population, yet all equal in the eyes of God and mine, they both differ and are simultaneously alike.

Each had a unique teaching message, each by way of example. There is no do-as-I-say, not-as-I-do philosophy in their world. Consequently, if your goal is a happy, serene life in accord, loving and respecting all of creation, put your mind and spirit into the animal's perspective. And stop talking so much. Only in the silence of your voice will you hear the *words* your dog speaks. Pay attention to the messages; they are priceless life lessons—the gift of wisdom.

If I wanted to list every lesson I learned from my four-pawed professors, psychologists, philosophers, and behaviorists, I'd have to write a book of several hundred pages. Instead, for the sake of time, I will synthesize.

Fritz, my first little doxie, taught me the worth of mind over matter. His lessons centered on mental toughness were my survival during a childhood laced with an embarrassing skin condition and resulting bullying, and the difficult adolescent years spent searching to find myself. Above all, he taught me to accept myself as I was, just as he did with his short legs and long torso. Appearance means nothing—it's who you are that matters, was his mantra.

Spartacus, aka Sparty, another member of the doxie pack, affectionately referred to as the alpha male leader, taught me the art of softening a strong authoritarian personality with subtle diplomacy essential for the acquisition of interpersonal relationship skills, the crux of success in all life situations. What an indispensable lesson for professional and personal accomplishment. Sparty didn't fight; he negotiated for peace—effectively.

Rommel, my loyal, reliable gentleman companion, demonstrated how to enjoy the present, whether a car ride with his human family and furry siblings, a romp in the icy snow, or just reclining on his pillow surrounded by his loved ones. Optimistic, he always veered toward the brightest spot in the room and taught the value of gratitude even for the tiniest of blessings.

Greta, my one female doxie, was a true class act, a lady who never sought confrontation and rarely raised her bark for supercilious matters of trite consequence. When she spoke, she mediated situations between the doxie boys. She taught me not to sweat the little stuff but to look for the positive and enjoy the day.

Shelby, my beaten, abused sweet Baby Girl pit bull, espoused the most precious commodities—compassion and empathy. Her eyes welled up in front of physical and psychological pain. No-grudge forgiveness and unconditional love were her heartbeats. She demonstrated how stereotyping and prejudice create only disunity, aggression, and rash, slanderous judgments. Hers was an "Okay, it happened. I learned, I overcame. Now let me move on and help other unjustly tortured souls."

Daniel, my Miracle Beagle, refused to squander today by dwelling in yesterday—a precious life lesson for man and animal. A frisky lad energized with a forgive-and-forget mindset, he believed life should be more than just serious moments and focusing on toxic individuals who seek to hurt others. Though with determination he fought with me to ban gas-chamber euthanasia in many states, he willingly embraced my philosophy that dogs should be dogs and enjoy the art of playing and stealing slippers, besides fulfilling the demand for personal appearances and events participation for his cause.

Bella, my young, beautiful, long-legged, runway-type Greyhound is in the process of discovering who she is. A relative newcomer to the family, she demonstrates patience with herself and others. Speaking out against the dog track where she was seriously injured then abandoned, she sheds a light on the demonic usurpation of innocent animals for monetary gain.

Each taught appreciation and gratitude for a loving family, nourishment, nurturing, long fresh-air walks, and a soft pillow upon which to rest. All taught me to be appreciative and grateful for the triple dose of love, nurturing, and attention they reciprocated. Everyone imparted their unique philosophies and distinct virtues, which have helped me become a better person, living each day with the wisdom of a man who experienced not one day less than ninety-five summers, though I recently turned sixty! Each confirms the incalculable value of animal rescue—open your arms and your door to an unparalleled experience of unconditional love and happiness.

With their strolls across the Rainbow Bridge, Shelby and Daniel's earthly lives may have reached the finish line, but their legacies are just at the starting point. As their emissary and spokesman, I intend to keep the torch burning—to continue where they paused to answer God's call. Via my motivational speaking, social media presence, and podcasts, I seek to encourage, empower, and inspire children, teens, and adults to live happy, fulfilling, well-balanced lives. Although I now walk alone to my speaking engagements, I am always in company: Shelby and Daniel are nestled in my words and spirit.

In God's eyes, there is equity and harmony in all creation. Let us honor His wishes. Let us make room in our hearts and homes for abandoned, neglected pups. The rewards are unimaginable—immeasurable!

Never, never be afraid to do what is right, especially if the well-being of a person or animal is at stake.

~ Dr. Martin Luther King Jr.

Joe Dwyer

Author, Motivational Speaker, Animal Advocate, Martial Artist

Affirmation: Daniel survived the lion's den/gas chamber, and Shelby turned beatings and abuse into a therapy dog vocation so each could help others in need.

Why not convert your adversity into a saving mission? And why not rescue the many amazing and inspiring pups waiting to love you?

More can be learned about Shelby and Daniel's amazing lives of hardship, struggle, survival, triumph, and giving back via my two books:

Shelby's Grace: From Abused Pup to Angel of Mercy
A Conversation with Daniel the Miracle Beagle

Website: www.joedwyerjr.com

PHOTOS

Joe and Shelby therapy visit

Daniel and Shelby

123

Daniel

Jenna, Joe, Shelby, Geralynn

Daniel and Shelby playing

Joe and Bella

Joe and Shelby

Joe and Daniel speaking at a rescue

Pit bull event: Joe, Shelby, Geralynn

Shelby May 2010

School visit

Shelby and my daughter Jenna

Shelby

Shelby school visit and talk

Shelby school visit, therapy for exams

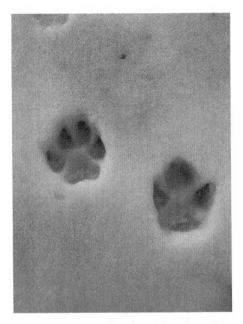

Shelby's pawprints in the snow the day she passed...

looks like an angel

Shelby "read to animals" event

Speaking at a school

Speaking to students at CCD

Made in the USA
Middletown, DE
28 September 2021

49288866R00090